SCIENCE, TECHNOLOGY AND INNOVATION POLICIES

YUGOSLAVIA

ORGANISATION FOR ECONOMIC CO-OPERATION AND DEVELOPMENT

Pursuant to article 1 of the Convention signed in Paris on 14th December, 1960, and which came into force on 30th September, 1961, the Organisation for Economic Co-operation and Development (OECD) shall promote policies designed:

- to achieve the highest sustainable economic growth and employment and a rising standard of living in Member countries, while maintaining financial stability, and thus to contribute to the development of the world economy;
- to contribute to sound economic expansion in Member as well as non-member countries in the process of economic development; and
- to contribute to the expansion of world trade on a multilateral, non-discriminatory basis in accordance with international obligations.

The original Member countries of the OECD are Austria, Belgium, Canada, Denmark, France, the Federal Republic of Germany, Greece, Iceland, Ireland, Italy, Luxembourg, the Netherlands, Norway, Portugal, Spain, Sweden, Switzerland, Turkey, the United Kingdom and the United States. The following countries acceded subsequently through accession at the dates hereafter: Japan (28th April, 1964), Finland (28th January, 1969), Australia (7th June, 1971) and New Zealand (29th May, 1973).

The Socialist Federal Republic of Yugoslavia takes part in some of the work of the OECD (agreement of 28th October, 1961).

Publié en français sous le titre:

POLITIQUES DE LA SCIENCE,
DE LA TECHNOLOGIE ET DE L'INNOVATION
YOUGOSLAVIE

This report is part of the OECD series of Science, Technology and Innovation Policy Reviews of individual Member countries.

These reviews have two purposes: first to enable the country or (region) concerned to appraise the institutions and mechanisms which influence various fields –scientific and industrial, but also economic, educational and social– and contribute to its technological development .

Second, the review helps to enrich the pool of available knowledge on the content of relevant policies. In this way OECD countries can derive lessons which will help them to perfect their own policies. Through this improved knowledge of the resources deployed by Member countries, the reviews help to strengthen international co-operation.

The reviews are undertaken at the request of governments, which contribute to their cost. Although a flexible approach is adopted in regard to the focus, the methodology and the presentation of these reviews, there is a common procedure for preparing and conducting them. The process of review consists of the following stages:

- The preparation of a General Report on the relevant features and policies of the country under review.
- An information mission: a team of Examiners visits the country under review and contacts decision makers, senior officials, industrialists and academics. The Examiners also visit a certain number of laboratories, universities, enterprises, and public and private institutions. The aim of this second stage is to supplement the information provided by the General Report and to enable the Examiners to formulate what they deem to be the main problems raised by the implementation of the policies under review: this constitutes the Examiners' Report.
- The presentation of the two reports to the OECD Committee for Scientific and Technological Policy, which then holds a Review Meeting at which representatives of the country under review answer questions put by the Examiners and the Delegates of Member countries.
- The publication (under the authority of the Secretary-General) of all documents relating to the review: the General Report, the Examiners' Report and the Account of the Review Meeting.

For the study of Yugoslavia, the team of Examiners included Mrs. Agnes Aylward, Director, Science and Technology Policy, Department of Industry and Commerce, Dublin, Ireland; Mr. Ricardo Galli, Professor, University of Milano, Italy; Mr. Martti M. Kaila, Professor, Helsinki University of Technology, Finland; Mr. Morten Knudsen, Director General, Technological Institute, Copenhagen, Denmark; and from the OECD Secretariat Mr. Jean-Eric Aubert (co-ordinator of the review) assisted by Mr. François Hetman (consultant).

The Examiners and the OECD Directorate for Science, Technology and Industry would like to express their gratitude to the Yugoslav Authorities, at Federal, Republican and Provincial levels, who have provided invaluable assistance in this study and prepared related reports, meetings and visits.

The Examiners would like also to thank the representatives of the scientific, industrial and labour communities for their great hospitality and very open discussion of the situation of their country.

Also available

REVIVAL THROUGH TECHNOLOGY (1988)
(70 88 02 1) ISBN 92-64-13103-5   228 pages   £12.00   US$22.00   F100.00   DM43.00

MAIN SCIENCE AND TECHNOLOGY INDICATORS
ISSN 1011-792X (Bi-annual, June and September)

Nᵒ 1/1982 – 1988 (September 1988)
Single issue not sold separately
1989 Subscription (2 issues)   £18.00   US$33.00   F150.00   DM65.00

REVIEWS OF NATIONAL SCIENCE AND TECHNOLOGY POLICY: DENMARK (1988)
(92 88 02 1) ISBN 92-64-13058-6   120 pages   10.50   US$19.80   F90.00   DM39.00

REVIEWS OF NATIONAL SCIENCE AND TECHNOLOGY POLICY: NETHERLANDS (1987)
(92 87 03 1) ISBN 92-64-12955-3   142 pages   £9.50   US$20.00   F95.00   DM35.00

REVIEWS OF NATIONAL SCIENCE AND TECHNOLOGY POLICY: FINLAND (1987)
(92 87 02 1) ISBN 92-64-12928-6   154 pages   £9.50   US$19.00   F95.00   DM42.00

REVIEWS OF NATIONAL SCIENCE AND TECHNOLOGY POLICY: SWEDEN (1987)
(92 87 04 1) ISBN 92-64-12958-8   112 pages   £6.00   US$13.00   F60.00   DM26.00

INNOVATION POLICY. WESTERN PROVINCES OF CANADA (1988)
(92 88 01 1) ISBN 92-64-13056-X   108 pages   £8.50   US$16.50   F75.00   DM32.00

INNOVATION POLICY: SPAIN (1987)
(92 87 06 1) ISBN 92-64-13029-2   106 pages   £7.00   US$15.00   F70.00   DM30.00

INNOVATION POLICY: IRELAND (1987)
(92 87 01 1) ISBN 92-64-12918-9   76 pages   £5.00   US$10.00   F50.00   DM22.00

EVALUATION OF RESEARCH.   A Selection of Current Practices (1987)
(92 87 05 1) ISBN 92-64-12981-2   78 pages   £5.00   US$11.00   F50.00   DM22.00

STI REVIEW – SCIENCE, TECHNOLOGY, INDUSTRY   ISSN 1010-5247 (half-yearly)

No. 1 – AUTUMN 1986
 • Technology and Jobs.
 • International Flows of Technology.
 • Science, Technology and Competitiveness.
   (90 86 01 1) ISBN 92-64-12888-3   130 pages   £8.00   US$16.00   F80.00   DM35.00

No. 2 – SEPTEMBER 1987
 • Technology and the Food Processing Industries.
 • Diffusing New Technologies – Micro-electronics.
 • Technology, Competitiveness and the Special Problems of Small Countries.
 • Innovative Activity, R&D and Patenting. The Evidence of the Survey on Innovation Diffusion
   in Italy.
 • Innovation Measures. A Tentative Appraisal.
   (90 87 01 1) ISBN 92-64-13002-0   174 pages   £8.00   US$16.00   F80.00   DM35.00

No. 3 – APRIL 1988
 • Structural Adjustment in the Automobile Industry.
 • New Materials in the Transport Sector.
 • The Technological and Economic Impact of the New Superconductors.
 • The Role of Information and TelecommunicationsTechnologies in Regional Development.
   (90 87 02 1)   ISBN 92-64-13094-2   174 pages   £12.90   US$24.20   F110.00   DM47.00
   1987 Subscription (No. 2 and No. 3) and
   1988 Subscription No. 4 and No. 5)   £15.00   US$30.00   F150.00   DM66.00

Prices charged at the OECD Bookshop.

THE OECD CATALOGUE OF PUBLICATIONS and supplements will be sent free of charge
on request addressed either to OECD Publications Service,
2, rue André-Pascal, 75775 PARIS CEDEX 16, or to the OECD Distributor in your country.

TABLE OF CONTENTS

Part I

GENERAL REPORT

Part II

EXAMINERS' REPORT

Part III
ACCOUNT OF THE REVIEW MEETING

LIST OF TABLES

7

LIST OF FIGURES

8

SPEECH TO THE REVIEW MEETING BY MR. BRANKO MIKULIC, PRESIDENT OF THE FEDERAL EXECUTIVE COUNCIL

Dubrovnik, 25th October 1987

Mr. Chairman, Ladies and Gentlemen, Comrades, I have the special pleasure of welcoming you on the occasion of this meeting which is very important for Yugoslavia, organised by the OECD Committee for Scientific and Technological Policy and devoted to a review of Yugoslavia's science, technology and innovation policies.

The fact that we have gathered here demonstrates that Yugoslavia is determined to rely on science, technology and innovation in addressing its social problems, primarily these relating to production.

This stems from the conviction prevalent in all strata of society that problems can be solved, and resources developed and utilised in the most efficient way through adequate scientific and technological development, combined with the further adaptation of Yugoslav enterprises to the rules of a market economy.

In our view it is precisely in a market economy that the synergistic features of the socialist self-management model will find their expression. The market economy model, coupled with incentives aimed at restructuring the economy and developing small and medium scale producers of goods and services, will further motivate all economic actors to increase their investments in scientific and technological development.

In order to achieve this, Yugoslavia will develop its own research and development capacities and join in international efforts in this area to the maximum extent possible. To that end we have adopted a policy of increasing expenditures on science and technology and eliminated restrictions on the growth of investments in science, at a time when, because of our material, structural and other difficulties, we are limiting all other forms of expenditure.

We have adopted the Strategy of Technological Development of Yugoslavia, as the first of a series of strategies, not by chance but rather with the intention for it to serve as the basis for all other development strategies that we are now adopting.

We have concluded on the basis of our own experience, as well as the experiences of other countries, that we should put all our intellectual production potential in the service of the well-being of mankind, of peace and international co-operation.

The effort of reviewing Yugoslavia's science, technology and innovation policies is the second to be carried out in co-operation with OECD and its Member countries.

We appreciate the documents that have been produced as a result of this co-operation. Yugoslavia's economic policy has been reviewed as a rule every year, and occasionally evaluations have also been undertaken of policies related to the areas of education, agriculture, environment, energy and industry.

In the Examiners' Report reviewing Yugoslavia's policies in the areas of science, technology and innovation, the question has been put: "Is Yugoslav non-alignment an island or a bridge?" We, dear friends, have no dilemmas whatsoever on that score. Yugoslavia is a European non-aligned country, but also a Mediterranean developing country. At the same time, Yugoslavia is at the crossroads and is the meeting place of European and Mediterranean paths, cultural traditions and history. We are making particular efforts to ensure that Yugoslavia takes part in all European and world events in the fields of politics, economy, culture, and, especially, science and technology. In view of its political philosophy and its consistent advocacy of the genuine principles of non-alignment which negate divisions of any kind and call for the broadest possible co-operation among all the countries of the world, Yugoslavia cannot be an isolated island. We firmly believe in a world of co-operation and mutual respect, in the dismantling of artificial barriers which still keep us apart, in the prevalence of reason and awareness that only together can we aspire to build a better and safer future.

Mr. Chairman, Ladies and Gentlemen, Comrades, Yugoslavia will do everything in its power to become a society founded on science and to further promote on that basis its social, cultural and other values. We are convinced that properly used technology in the hands of conscientious men will never jeopardize mankind. Thank you.

YUGOSLAVIA: REPUBLICS AND AUTONOMOUS PROVINCES

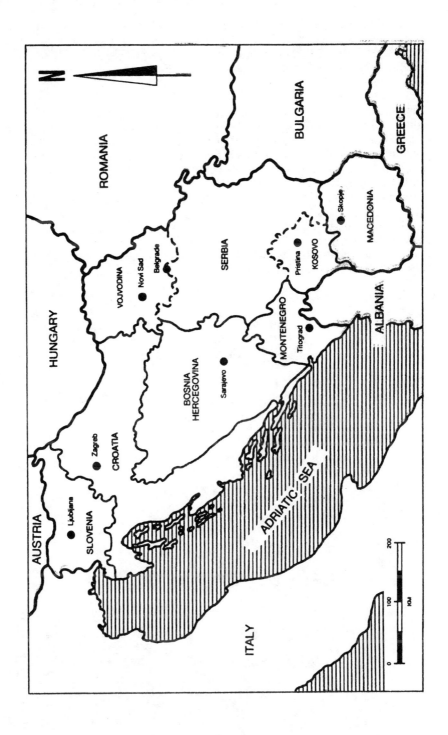

Part I

GENERAL REPORT

This document, provided by the Yugoslav authorities, was prepared by the Mihajlo Pupin Institute, Belgrade, and the Institute for Economic Research, Ljubljana. Contributions to the document were made by Vlastimir Matejic and Lojze Socan (editors), Predrag Radivojevic, Milojko Lazic, Djuro Kutlaca, Vedran Kraljeta, Peter Stanovnik, Stanka Kukar and Dusanka Maleric. The preparation of the document was financed by the Council of the Association of the Communities for Science. The text has been edited by the OECD Secretariat.

1. THE SOCIO-ECONOMIC DEVELOPMENT OF YUGOSLAVIA

1. Post-war development characteristics of Yugoslavia's economy

In order to understand better the broader economical and political climate for technological development in Yugoslavia it seems appropriate to review briefly the basic phases of the post-war development of the Yugoslav economy. This survey takes into account trends and qualitative turning points of the world economy and its impacts on the Yugoslav economy.

During the period of post-war reconstruction and in the first half of the 1950s, the development strategy was based on the then common theory of industrialisation of socialist countries. However, the economic blockade of Yugoslavia by socialist countries after 1948 led to the adoption of the concept of self-sufficient development and industrialisation (in spite of suboptimal conditions for such development).

The period of general industrialisation emphasizing the development of manufacturing, in the second half of the 1950s and in the first half of the 1960s, witnessed the swiftest growth

Table 1. **Indicators of economic growth = 1956-84**
Per cent

Indicators	Average annual growth rate				
	1956-84	1956-64	1965-72	1973-79	1980-84
Gross domestic product[1], (1972 prices)	5.9	8.8	6.0	6.1	0.4
GDP per capita, (1972 prices)	4.9	7.7	5.0	5.1	−0.3
GDP in industry, (1972 prices)	7.4	12.2	6.6	7.5	2.1
GDP in agriculture, (1972 prices)	2.5	3.6	2.0	2.2	2.9
Employment	3.5	6.4	2.2	4.1	3.1
Employment in industry	3.8	6.6	2.2	4.1	3.1
Labour productivity in public sector	3.2	4.8	4.3	2.7	−2.0
Real personal incomes	3.6	6.3	6.1	2.7	−2.0
Retail prices	15.4	5.1	10.1	16.9	41.6
Cost of living	16.0	6.9	10.6	17.3	40.1
Fixed assets public sector[2]	8.0	8.8	8.2	7.9	4.5
Exports of goods	14.0	12.8	10.1	14.0	2.2
Imports of goods	14.2	11.1	15.1	16.2	−6.9

1. According to Yugoslav methodology, Gross Domestic Product (GDP) is created only in material production and does not include some services (health, education, administration, part of financial and business services) which are included in GDP in OECD countries.
2. For this indicator, the last column gives data for the period 1980-83.
Source: All data except as otherwise mentioned are derived from the Statistical Yearbook of Yugoslavia for appropriate years. Calculations were done at the Institute for Economic Research, Ljubljana.

Figure 1. PRODUCTION FUNCTION OF THE YUGOSLAV ECONOMY – 1948-84

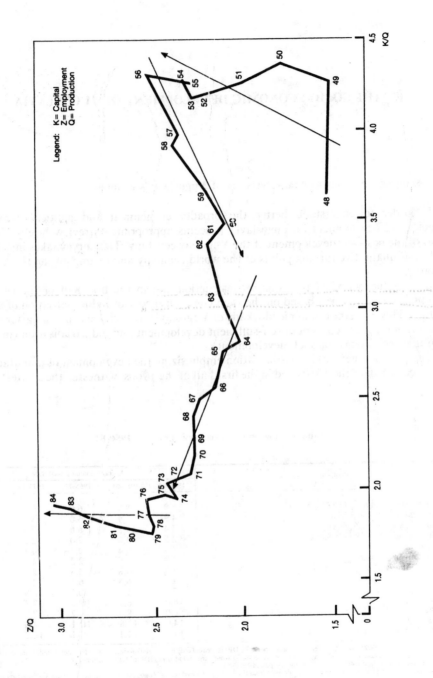

Legend: K = Capital
Z = Employment
Q = Production

Source: Mencinger, J., in *Economic Systems and Economic Efficiency*, Gospodarska gibanja, No. 154, Ljubljana, September 1985.

16

of productivity (4.8 per cent annually over the period 1955-65), capital efficiency and hence economic growth (8.8 per cent average annual rate of growth of gross domestic product). These accomplishments reflected the new initiative in self-management working organisations and changes in production capacity, abandonment of coercive collectivisation in agriculture, the low cost of basic imported factors of production (energy and capital) as well as increased domestic and foreign demand for Yugoslav goods, especially from the EEC countries. In the mid-1960s, the Yugoslav economy reached the stage of maturity for structural and qualitative transformation; from extensive development and "quantitative planning" to "planning of qualitative development processes", with emphasis on lowering costs on one side, and improving quality, and technical standards of goods and services, on the other.

The second half of the 1960s and the early 1970s, until the beginning of the first oil crisis, was characterised by a continuing substantial rate of economic growth (6.0 per cent annual growth of GDP over the period 1965-73). After unsuccessful attempts to open the national economy through economic reform in 1965, Yugoslavia continued to stick to the old elements of economic interventionism: large disparities of productive factor prices, import substitution and quantitative restrictions on imports. The result was an above-average growth of real personal incomes, substantially faster growth of imports (15.1 per cent) than exports (10.0 per cent) and a decrease of capital formation.

In the 1970s, traditional economic interventionism, which undervalued domestic and foreign capital and energy, resulted in a strong expansion of capital, energy and import-intensive capacity while disregarding rapid price increases in these factors on the world market. Inadequate internal criteria for resource allocation also led to duplication of production capacities in Yugoslavia's individual republics and provinces.

These trends, coupled with the absence of responsibility for unsuccessful investment projects on the part of the republics, provinces and enterprises resulted in significantly increased costs of production and in a heavy international indebtedness of the Yugoslav economy. They also led to a decrease in Yugoslavia's export competitiveness, its rate of investment and its subsequent ability to develop. Yugoslav exports to OECD countries declined strongly: the export-import ratio in trade with OECD countries reached a low point of 49 per cent in 1979.

With these deficiencies, Yugoslavia entered the 1980s. The main feature of this period, particularly in the highly developed countries, is the contribution of new technologies and innovations to economic growth. Yugoslavia's economic structure, with high consumption of energy, raw materials, capital and labour per unit of production together with obsolete technological standards, and low quality goods and services has resulted in extremely high costs and low value added. Insufficient investment in marketing has contributed to low prices on foreign markets. This fact, coupled with an unsatisfactorily low rate of domestic savings has led to a decrease in purchasing power and to a decrease in investment as a fraction of GDP.

Therefore, the question of a more market-oriented economy and acceptance of international development criteria – as laid down in the Long-term Programme of Economic Stabilisation established at the federal level – has become a condition *sine qua non* for maintaining contacts and partner status between Yugoslavia and advanced economies. With economic and political support for sound enterprises, there is a possibility of restoring economic growth; strengthening structural and technological revitalisation of the economy; increasing productivity, efficiency, exports and employment; reducing the burden of the foreign debt and finding a gradual solution to structural, social and regional problems.

17

Table 2. **Changes in economic structure – 1956-84**

Sector	Percentage of GDP				
	1956	1965	1973	1980	1984
Primary	33.3	21.9	18.5	14.5	15.7
Secondary	34.1	44.5	45.1	50.1	50.0
Tertiary	32.6	33.6	36.4	35.4	34.3

Source: See Table 1.

Table 3. **GDP and expenditures – 1956-84[1]**

Period	Consumption			Gross investment			
	Total	Personal consumption	Public consumption[2]	Total	Production branches	Equipment in production branches	Non-production branches
1956-64	62.7	51.8	11.0	31.9	–	–	–
1965-72	62.9	53.8	9.0	30.1	20.7	10.6	9.4
1973-79	63.9	54.4	9.5	34.1	24.0	12.6	10.1
1980-84	60.3	51.5	8.8	28.8	20.5	9.8	8.3

1. Percentages of non-production consumption and investment do not add to 100 per cent due to average values for individual periods, surpluses or deficits in the trade balance, changes of inventories and statistical errors.
2. Material costs.
Source: See Table 1.

Table 4. **External debt – 1974-84**

Year	External debt of Yugoslavia, end of year data (million dollars)				Debt burden ratios (per cent)			
	External debt, total	Total inflow of resources	Total outflow of resources (debt)	Interest payments in total debt service payments	External debt/GDP service payments	External debt/Exports of goods and services	Debt service/- Current foreign exchange receipts	Interest payments/- Current foreign exchange receipts
1974	1 780	1 873	1 367	291	17.2	118	–	7.6
1977	7 934	2 973	1 767	381	20.8	142	22	7.3
1979	15 232	4 333	3 159	821	21.5	174	24	12.0
1980	18 873	5 342	3 819	1 281	25.7	181	27	14.3
1981	21 096	4 458	4 304	2 107	29.2	209	32	19.2
1982	20 341	3 166	4 238	2 149	31.0	200	36	20.0
1983	20 577	4 627	4 640	1 711	–	202	40	17.3
1984	20 191	3 505	5 223	1 854	–	195	42	18.0

Source: Kovacevic, Z.: *The External Debt of Yugoslavia,* Development and South-South Co-operation, Vol. 1., No. 1, Research Centre for Co-operation with Developing Countries, Ljubljana, December 1985.

2. Challenges of the world economy

The post-war economic interventionism of Yugoslavia, based on import substitution, internal criteria for development, controlled prices, and administrative allocation of capital, was successful in the 1950s and 1960s, i.e. in the period of economic growth which was rapid and extensive, although quantitatively regulated. This interventionism involved a strategy of rapid industrialisation, based on providing capital and mass industrial employment.

However, this type of interventionism was not capable of establishing (nor carrying out) the qualitative transformation of Yugoslavia's economy. As in other advanced economies, such a transformation must take into account international investment and development criteria, be based on a rational use of all factors of production, and give a predominant role to technology in determining competitive economic capacities. Only such long-term economic policies can allow the Yugoslav economy to preserve its share of advanced economies' markets, and stimulate rapid development of all fields of knowledge. Suitable conditions for such a qualitative transformation of the economy were created in the mid-1960s.

In the period 1945-85, Yugoslavia developed significant industrial capacity and competence, technical knowledge, research infrastructure and management competence. At the same time, from being a backward agricultural country, Yugoslavia became an industrial country and increased its participation in international production and trade. However, Yugoslavia did not succeed in carrying out the qualitative and structural transformation of its economy. It failed:

- In the 1960s, when ideal conditions prevailed: domestic (high economic growth, low rate of unemployment, export opportunities) and international (low prices of energy, raw materials and capital, high import demand).

- In the 1970s, when the high cost of energy, technology, labour and capital made structural and qualitative transformation necessary. In this period, many similar or even less developed economies successfully achieved structural and qualitative transformations of their economies through long-term policies of real prices for production factors, through a relative opening of their economies and through export promotion.

- In the first half of the 1980s, when economies oriented towards import substitution began to lose their competitiveness on world markets, mainly because of inefficient use of factors of production and increased technological obsolescence.

The fact that the interventionist policies did not enhance structural and qualitative adaptation, had several consequences:

- *Structural weakness*

  Investment criteria based on inadequate assessment of factors of production, especially capital (domestic and foreign), and energy, led to haphazard development of production capacities which are now unable to meet real costs of production, to bring about technological revitalisation, to boost exports or to secure further growth. At the same time, only a small part of the economy was involved in efficient co-operation with foreign enterprises in the areas of technology, production, finance, marketing, etc.

– *Technology lag*

This is particularly serious in the case of the technologies likely to contribute to the growth of productivity. It is reflected not only in the field of computers and other electronic equipment in industry and research institutes, but also in the inefficient use of existing modern equipment, caused by lack of knowledge.

– *Loss of competitiveness*

The lack of motivation to make production and management more efficient has resulted in extremely high production costs for the greater part of Yugoslav exports. Yugoslavia lags behind successful world exporters in technological standards, quality, design, marketing, etc. In Yugoslavia's exports to the OECD markets, the share of goods with above-average unit value decreased from about 20 per cent to about 10 per cent during the period 1979-84, while the share of goods in the under-average price range increased from about 60 per cent to 70 per cent.

– *Inefficient use of knowledge and human capital*

As a consequence of the lack of competitiveness, Yugoslavia's economy failed to take advantage of its existing research and development capacities and scientific institutions, which were already adequately equipped and staffed in the 1950s and 1960s. Research, development and innovation were not generally a decisive factor in the survival and growth of enterprises. Some 80 per cent of R&D personnel remained at the universities and institutes, i.e. outside the economy. With some exceptions, this did not lead to long-term co-operation between science and economy. The relatively high investment in R&D activities (about 1 per cent of GDP) was seen as more of an added cost than a necessary investment for increased productivity and competitiveness. Nevertheless, there are enterprises and exporters who are ahead in technology and innovation and who, in addition to their own R&D capacities, co-operate successfully with other domestic and foreign partners on a permanent basis. These arrangements were established on the premise of a long-term involvement in exports, especially exports to the most demanding world markets.

Table 5. **Indicators of socio-economic change – 1953-85**

Indicators	1953	1971	1981	1985
Percentage of economically active population	46.3	43.3	44.0	–
Percentage of agricultural population	60.9	38.2	19.9	–
Percentage of illiterate population aged 10 years and over	25.4	15.1	9.5	–
Percentage of population with a two-year post secondary school or university education	0.6	2.8	5.6	–
Rate of natural increase of population per 1 000 inhabitants	16.0	9.5	7.5	6.8
Deaths per 1 000 inhabitants	12.4	8.7	9.0	9.1
Infant deaths per 1 000 live births	116.1	49.5	30.8	28.4
Life expectancy at birth (years)	58.1	67.8	70.4	–
Inhabitants per physician[1]	2 262	993	667	601
Inhabitants per hospital bed[1]	279	171	163	164

1. For these indicators, the last column gives 1984 data.
Source: See Table 1.

3. Regional differences in the socio-economic development of Yugoslavia

There are historical reasons for the very different levels of development in the various parts of Yugoslavia after World War II. Slovenia and northern parts of Croatia and Serbia inherited a relatively strong industrial base, well-developed transportation and utilities infrastructures and a high level of education. The southern part of the country was almost completely based on obsolete agriculture, handicrafts, and in some places on obsolete production of minerals and raw materials.

Large differences in regional development have required the implementation of an active regional policy. The rapid development of the less-developed republics and Province of Kosovo is a priority. It is estimated that about 3 per cent of GDP is spent on promoting the development of less-developed regions through the Federal Fund for Development of Economically Less-Developed Republics and Kosovo, and through the federal budget as well as through monetary, foreign trade and taxation policies. Significant results have been achieved, especially in Bosnia-Herzegovina, Montenegro and Macedonia. Kosovo still lags behind.

In spite of this progress, differences in the level of development have not decreased as planned, while in some regions further undesirable deepening of differences has occurred (see Table 6). The major trends can be summarized as follows:

- Demographic differences between republics and provinces (which are still great) have decreased gradually;
- Differences in development of productive capacities have increased despite the orientation of economic policy to develop productive capacities in underdeveloped regions;
- Differences in economic achievement have increased particularly in terms of rates of employment; and
- Differences in the standard of living have decreased.

As a result of a policy of equalization of living conditions, the differences in average personal income per employee in the different regions are less significant than could be expected. Labour in less developed regions is relatively expensive, even though it is abundant (high unemployment rates and overpopulation in agricultural regions). In the past, capital earmarked for less-developed regions was relatively cheaper, since the regional policies included measures aimed at reducing capital costs (lower interest rates, subsidies, long repayment times). These policies were intended to attract potential investors to less-developed regions. But they had also a negative side since they did not stimulate the use of the most abundant factor of production in these regions (i.e. labour). In addition to the unwise selection of projects, large and expensive industrial plants were built which increased rather than solved the problems of these regions.

The most important development factors differ widely from one region to another. In particular, these include labour and know-how, existing production structures and the technological level of development, integration into international trade, business efficiency, rate of capital investment and long-term indebtedness. Indicators of the development potentials of the republics and autonomous provinces in the early 1980s are shown in the Table 6.

As regards formal education of workers, the less-developed republics and Kosovo are apparently in a better position than the developed republics, where there are fewer workers

21

Table 6. **Regional differences in socio-economic development**

	Yugoslavia	Bosnia-Herzegovina	Monte Negro	Croatia	Macedonia	Slovenia	Serbia without provinces	Kosovo	Vojvodina
Demographic changes									
Natural increase of population, 1981 (per cent)	0.8	1.1	1.2	0.3	1.3	0.6	0.4	2.5	0.2
Agricultural population, 1981 (per cent)	19.1	17.3	13.5	15.2	21.7	9.4	27.6	24.6	
Illiterate population age 10 years and over, 1981 (per cent)	9.5	14.5	9.4	5.6	10.9	0.8	11.1	17.6	5.8
Level of development of production base									
Active fixed assets per person capable of work, 1983[1]	100.0	81.7	120.2	124.5	69.3	206.5	79.6	43.4	103.9
Investment in fixed assets related to GDP, 1981-83 (per cent)	26.3	32.8	48.6	25.9	27.1	20.8	24.1	49.9	24.4
Unemployment rate, 1984 (per cent)	13.5	18.8	19.1	7.2	21.1	1.9	14.6	33.3	13.6
Results of production forces									
GDP per capita, 1983[1]	100.0	68.6	77.1	124.8	65.2	197.0	98.9	28.0	120.4
Efficiency of investment in fixed assets, 1983[1]	100.0	81.8	67.2	99.8	98.2	101.2	116.8	70.7	110.8
Standard of living									
Male life expectancy at birth, 1979-80 (years)	67.7	67.7	71.4	66.9	68.4	67.3	69.5	68.7	67.4
Net personal income per worker in public sector, 1984[1]	100.0	92.7	80.5	108.3	78.8	121.7	94.4	78.3	102.4
Average size of housing per capita, 1981 (square meters)	16.8	13.4	14.4	19.6	15.7	19.9	16.9	10.3	21.7
Indicators of education									
Youth in secondary, 2-year post-secondary schools & universities in population capable of work, 1981 (per cent)	8.7	9.7	9.6	8.0	9.6	8.9	7.6	12.7	7.2
Workers with a 2-year post-secondary school qualification and university education in enterprises, 1983 (per cent)	7.1	6.8	7.6	7.3	7.5	5.8	7.9	6.2	6.5
Funds for on-the-job training per worker, 1982[1]	100.0	270.0	61.8	144.1	12.7	181.4	22.5	87.3	35.3
Technical-technological intensity of industry									
Automated equipment (per cent)	4.7	3.1	3.7	6.4	3.3	6.4	3.9	3.9	4.8
Equipment, not older than 4 years (per cent)	40.2	39.2	36.2	40.5	42.1	34.8	42.2	34.9	39.9
Export orientation of industry									
Income of exports in total exchanges (per cent)	12.1	10.0	12.5	11.1	7.9	14.7	14.6	11.0	6.3
Convertible currency exports in total exports, 1982 (per cent)	48.0	46.8	25.1	59.4	42.7	72.3	50.8	21.5	53.4
Business efficiency									
Available gross accumulation per worker, 1982[1]	100.0	87.9	71.8	104.7	82.6	131.1	96.9	55.1	94.3
Long-term loans in total long-term assets (per cent)	27.5	29.5	47.0	22.8	27.0	10.3	26.5	23.9	36.1

1. In these indicators, the total for Yugoslavia is taken as 100 per cent.
Source: See Table 1.

with university education or advanced qualifications and where the average number of years of education of all workers is smaller. Slovenia, according to these criteria, ranks last and next to last, respectively. However, the more developed republics allocate more funds for on-the-job training (with the exception of Bosnia-Herzegovina). In the past, education spread very rapidly in less-developed regions, so that the proportion of the employable youth population attending school has increased.

In the early 1980s, the proportion of young people attending school was nearly equal in all regions. However, the quality of education has not been maintained during the rapid extension of education, and the actual qualifications of people in less-developed regions are lower than their formal education would suggest. This is reflected in low efficiency and low labour productivity. A major task in future development of the less-developed regions is to raise the standard of education and to establish on-the-job training.

Strategies of technological, economic and social development in Yugoslavia must take into account regional differences so that more jobs are provided in less developed regions, especially in small-scale industry and tertiary activities.

Joint ventures involving enterprises from developed and less-developed regions should be directed towards creation of new jobs in technologically advanced and efficient productions. These can obtain 60 per cent of all funds from the Fund for Development of Economically Less-developed Republics and Kosovo. Through such joint ventures, technological and organisational know-how should be transferred from developed to less developed regions in order to improve the business efficiency and export orientation of less developed regions.

II. SCIENCE, TECHNOLOGY AND SOCIETY IN YUGOSLAVIA

This chapter summarises the basic principles, structural characteristics and institutional variables in Yugoslavia which have determined:
- the scientific and technological policy of Yugoslavia, during the past 15 years;
- the scope, nature and quality of scientific and technological results; and
- the response of the science and technology system to expectations put on it, both by itself and by society.

1. Federal structure and decision-making system

The first and most important principle is Yugoslavia's federal structure and its decentralised self-management decision-making. This principle has been strictly adhered to and the results have been considerable. The most important effects of this principle are described below.

Scientific and technological policies (explicitly expressed, or implied in other policies) have been formulated independently and individually by each separate federal unit, with a very small or negligible degree of interrelation and co-ordination. This approach accorded with generally self-reliant attitudes and policies, and with the belief that science is one of the cultural values which should be a factor in development. As a consequence, during the last 15 years Yugoslav scientific and technological policy has been the sum of the scientific and technologic policies of the federal units. In other words, a distinct national policy as such did not exist. And since there was no national scientific and technological policy, no funds were required to implement such a policy. The adoption of this approach resulted in the elimination of national funds for research and development. Agencies and organisations dealing with scientific and technological policy at the national level ceased their activities. National institutes became republic or municipal institutes.

A second consequence of the above principle was a reduction in the bureaucracy involved in the process of formulation and implementation of scientific and technological policies. Decentralisation naturally involved larger numbers of people and organisations in the formulation of scientific and technological policy. This radically reduced earlier bureaucratic structures, institutions and procedures. However, this process went too far, because the elimination of well-established procedures resulted in a lack of organisation which significantly reduced the otherwise positive consequences.

One consequence of decentralisation was an increase of interest in science and technology at the level of federal units and regions. But the economic system and policies of those units and regions were not sufficiently encouraging to enhance this interest. A decentralised system for scientific and technological policy can be very effective only if the system is ready and able to take initiatives.

As a result of decentralisation, proposals and plans were set up for a comprehensive system of scientific and technological organisations and institutions of each federal unit. This stimulated the growth of research capacities (in terms of numbers of research staff) but also had the negative effect of duplication of research resources, institutions, projects, etc. This duplication was often an obstacle to reaching "critical masses" within regions and was also detrimental to research systems in other regions. Decreased concentration of scientific and technological capacities weakened and fragmented research capability. This led to lower efficiency, decreased quality of research, etc. Most attempts to reach the necessary "critical mass" involved lowering the entry qualifications at R&D centres with a consequent decline in standards. The belief that the market for R&D services would positively select and secure the highest standard of research results was only partly justified.

Unco-ordinated development of R&D capacity hampered the general technological development of the Yugoslav economy. As a result of the weakened research potential, technologies that needed to be purchased abroad could not be competently and authoritatively assessed. Decentralisation with closed regional systems and autonomous decision-making led to a lack of co-ordination in the purchase, import and diffusion of technology. Before the beginning of the 1980s it was the rule, rather than the exception, that Yugloslavia purchase the same technologies from several sources in different countries, in each case accepting very strict regulations for their use. Deficiencies in domestic technologies necessitated the import of foreign technologies. Given the country's weak bargaining power, the technologies purchased were often barely competitive and even obsolescent. This explains several severe economic "failures", which were first and foremost failures in purchasing appropriate foreign technologies.

Decentralisation, together with administrative management of economic development, destroyed the technological unity of the larger operations, primarily the major infrastructure systems (railways, post and telecommunications, electricity and water utilities, etc.) and created complex industrial systems with almost no internal technological co-ordination. For its size and level of economic development, Yugoslavia has, for example, a large number of manufacturers in the automobile industry who co-operate very little and depend primarily on foreign technology. The same situation occurs in the electrical and electronics industry, chemicals and especially the pharmaceutical industry.

On the positive side, decentralisation of social structures exposed science and technology to the attention and critical assessment of different interest groups. This helped research organisations to overcome the obstacles which stood between them and some segments of the society. Transparency of work, including presentation of work plans to the public at large, oriented the research organisations towards the development of a capability to recognise the interests and expectations of other parts of the society, and to work out approaches to meet these requirements and expectations. However, this development of relations between science and society was only partly effective, and generally resulted in a focus on short-term interests and research needs. The needs for longer-term economic development were not considered to any great extent.

2. Integration of research with social development

The second basic principle is the total integration of research with social development (economic, cultural, political, educational, etc.). This principle was institutionalised by establishing Self-management Communities of Interest for Science (SCIS) in order to:

- express the individual and collective needs of all sections of society for research findings;
- establish how these needs may be met;
- select short-term and long-term goals, research programmes and projects, producers and users of research findings; and
- define the criteria and procedures for the evaluation and utilisation of research work and research findings.

The establishment of these communities was provided for by law. Implementation of this principle has yielded the following results:

- First, there was a very intensive democratisation of the formulation of scientific and technological policy. However, this had some undesirable effects, because it was limited to small entities which acted mostly in a self-sufficient way, focussing on short-term goals and influenced by special interest groups.
- Second, the principle was realised only in formal terms. Research organisations expressed an increasing interest in satisfying the needs of the users of scientific results. Had these users demanded long-term and good quality scientific results during the 1970s and at the beginning of the 1980s, research work in Yugoslavia today would have been extensively incorporated into the economic and social fabric. The lack of demand for science and research results wrecked the essential effect of this principle.
- Third, the capability of research organisations to survive increased even when the budget was reduced or discontinued. This led to some organisations accepting and carrying out non-research tasks (designing, engineering, production, etc.), to the detriment of advanced training of research personnel.

An important side effect of this consequence, is the philosophy of the "zero-sum game" which is shared almost by all those responsible for research planning and allocation of funds of the communities of interest for science. Given the modest funds available, this philosophy has become dominant. It often results in minor research projects, since the primary goal is survival of the scientific organisation, and projects are merely a means of reaching that goal.

The current economic and development policies of Yugoslavia require explicit compliance with this principle, because there is a firm belief that no single part of the society can successfully develop without utilisation of research results, particularly domestic research. All economically important activities should use science and modern technology. As a consequence, research activities now have much better conditions for development; demand, reception and application of scientific results is wider and of better quality; and the capacity of scientific and technological institutions to solve domestic problems is increasing.

3. Openness of the scientific and technological system

The third principle is the openness of the scientific and technological system. Every research organisation within this system is completely independent in its decision making and planning, and is open to societal influences. This principle has created possibilities for co-operation inside the country, but relations between the users and the producers of research results are mostly limited to the level of federal units. International co-operation is possible but has not been sufficiently co-ordinated in terms of quality.

A first consequence of this principle is the multiplicity of arrangements between research and other organisations. There are several shortcomings in this respect: the small number of co-operative arrangements between research organisations except where such arrangements increase the chances for obtaining funds; the prevalence of short-term arrangements; other unclearly regulated relations between obligations and rights; and lack of mobility of the research staff.

A second consequence is a radical reduction of external bureaucracy in the planning and implementation of co-operative action. This is a benefit. However, there are also negative aspects. The suppression of structures considered to be bureaucratic also eliminated many useful norms, standards and informal rules. This is especially evident in international scientific and technological co-operation.

A third and the most important consequence of this principle is the rapid growth (especially during the 1970s) in the importation of technology, since the openness of technological system coupled with an over-valued domestic currency encouraged manufacturers to purchase rather than develop new technologies. Self-sufficient economic and technological development within the country and free access to foreign technology often led to a preference for acquisition (mostly purchase) of technology. This made it possible to follow more closely the development of technologies in the world, but at the same time it weakened the norms and standards for the purchase and use of foreign technologies. The Yugoslav economy became well supplied with technologies embodied in machines and equipment, and strongly dependent on foreign countries. Many market, commercial and other restrictions were accepted, e.g. production was conditional on purchase of input material. Incompatible technologies were acquired and domestic research potential to develop competitive technologies declined. Thus, the advantages of an open system, left without any real protection, had more negative than positive effects.

4. Structural characteristics

The location of research capacity has been determined by the structure established during the first post-war years. At that time the system of government scientific institutes (i.e. excluding industrial research organisations) was built up according to the principles of the planned economy and acquired large research staffs and laboratory equipment. The present situation, which has persisted for some time, is described below.

The greatest research potential – measured by full-time equivalent (FTE) research personnel – is in the independent institutes (50 per cent). The universities have a lesser but otherwise impressive 28 per cent and the lowest is in industry (22 per cent). This structural characteristic is the most critical for the efficient application, transfer and dissemination of technology.

The geographical location of research capacities is another important element. With the exception of Serbia, the better-developed the region the better is its research potential. This is partly due to the very nature of the research potential. It is also the result of policies aimed at avoiding further deepening of differences in economic and technological development between regions.

The research structure by type of R&D activity changed radically after the suppression of federal R&D funds. Independent institutes and university research centres were compelled to contract their R&D services to industry. According to the official statistics, the share of fundamental research decreased, while that of applied research increased and the share of development remained stable. The importance of activities with only a partial R&D component (design, engineering, consultancy, production, feasibility studies, etc.) also increased. As a result of these changes, which in principle were desirable because Yugoslavia needed more applied research and development than fundamental research, the situation by the beginning of the 1980s was the following:

- fundamental research decreased, and experimental research declined more than theoretical research;
- applied research increased, but most often without producing satisfactory applicable results; and
- development remained stable, but its real results were far below the needs of the Yugoslav economy, which had to be met mostly by imported technology. This is more the cause than the consequence of insufficient domestic research.

Demands for change were also strong in other sciences; particularly social sciences and humanities. However in these areas the possibilities for any substantial change were, and remain, much smaller.

For a long time, Yugoslav research organisations have been strongly inclined towards basic research rather than to mission-oriented research. This reflects primarily the cultural attitude towards the role of science: science should deal only with essential (i.e. theoretical) problems of knowledge. This attitude is particularly strong in the less-developed regions and federal units (Slovenia and Montenegro being the two extremes). This cultural attitude is accompanied by a weak demand (in scope and requirements) for domestic research results, especially in technology. As a consequence, research activities were sometimes undertaken mainly in order to justify previous choices and attitudes concerning, for example, technology, new capacities, pricing policy, organisation of work and management, economic and other measures, social reorganisation, etc.

During the past two decades the research structure has shifted from fundamental research in natural sciences and humanities to technological research. The share of other scientific fields (medicine, and biology) has remained stable since the mid-1970s, in terms of research funds, but in terms of FTE researchers there has been a shift towards medical and less technological sciences. The total number of FTE research workers has increased in all scientific fields. This is a very positive development given the nature of the problems to be solved by the Yugoslav economy and society.

The overall assessment of the current situation of structural characteristics of the scientific and technological system is the following:

- In terms of FTE researchers, the research potential is not negligible given the size of population, the number of employed persons and the economic development of the country.
- As to the regional distribution, the more developed federal units have relatively better research potential and vice versa. The exception to this rule was the change in the status of former "federal" institutes. These became institutes of the federal unit in which they were located. It is possible that, in the near future, there will be a need for national research organisations. However this need probably will be met by assigning joint national research tasks to certain existing institutes, which are now working both formally and structurally as republic or local units.
- Both in absolute and relative terms, the number of research centres in industry is small. This is a major concern. A significant increase in research capacity by those who are the prime users of R&D results (mainly production organisations) ranks

high on the list of priorities of future science and technology policies of Yugoslavia.

- The breakdown of research by discipline does not correspond to the level of development and the needs of Yugoslavia's economy and society. The share of technological research is far from satisfactory and the same goes for biological research. Research in natural sciences should be determined by long-term technological and other developmental needs rather than by a mere search for knowledge. Research in social sciences, especially in economics and law is well developed, judging by the number of researchers and available funds, but the contribution of social sciences to societal needs (particularly with regard to technological development) is much smaller than it should be.

5. Institutional factors

Institutional factors have had an important influence on the development and utilisation of scientific potential, and on the science and technology system. A brief discussion follows of the consequences of four institutional variables: Self-management Communities of Interest for Science; governmental bodies for science and technology; public procurement; and political and social actions concerning science and technology.

Self-management Communities of Interest for Science are societal (which means non-governmental) organisations. They are a part of the Yugoslav social organisation system aimed at the strengthening of the basic principle of integration of scientific research work with economic and social activities. To this end, these communities for science were created in the mid-1970s at the level of each federal unit, and an association of these communities was established at the federal level. In addition, communities for science can be found at the level of regions (at a lower level than federal units), at the level of municipalities, and for certain economic sectors, for groups of enterprises and even for important individual R&D undertakings.

The aim of these communities is to establish a continuous interaction between producers and users of research results (research organisations, on the one side, and industrial and other organisations on the other). Delegates jointly plan research activities, take decisions on their implementation and evaluation. During the past 13 years this system has been functioning in the following way:

- More than 20 per cent of research and development costs are financed through this system.
- These communities have provided all the funds (but at a very modest level) for the research projects for which there are no direct and immediate users (fundamental, cultural-historical research, and part of social research), and have financed in part (from 25 per cent up to a maximum 50 per cent) research of wider social interest, having direct users.
- The mechanism of financing has in large part determined the internal structure of these communities: special bodies are constituted by scientific disciplines (natural, technical, social, etc.) and by area of activity (planning and policy, international co-operation, investment, advanced training of research personnel, scientific publications). The funds available to these communities have been limited and have been decreasing. This has created complex problems concerning programmes, project selection and allocation of funds.

29

- It has proved difficult to change the vested interests of certain scientific fields and research organisations. As a result, the communities have generally continued to function in line with established groups and objectives, rather than changing them.
- Communities for science at the level of federal units enact five-year plans which are, theoretically, oriented towards solving problems relating to the social, economic, cultural and general development of society. The effect of vested interests has been to modify the plans significantly and to reduce significantly the level of efficiency and the social utility of funds allocated to these communities. This has been aggravated by the limitation of available funds which has hampered the emergence of major breakthroughs in R&D.
- Insufficient demand for scientific results, due to the excessive preference for imported technology is the main reason why these communities financed the existing research system through programmes and projects which were not the expression of real needs of industry and society, but more or less a justification for allocation of funds to the research organisations.
- Given such relationships, mechanisms for research evaluation had to adopt lower criteria so that almost any offered result was accepted. In only a few cases, was the financing of a project within the programme of these communities withdrawn. However, none of the beneficiaries returned funds which were incorrectly or inefficiently used.
- The communities for science, especially at the regional level, contributed to the development of research capacities outside the large cities and the regionalisation of science. A more important result of the presence of regional communities is streamlining the decision-making process and encouraging those research workers in small towns who would otherwise, for many reasons, hesitate to ask for programme and financial support from central bodies and funds.

In short, the SCIS are, according to the principles they are based upon, a modern and promising mechanism. So far this mechanism has been only partly exploited, because of the modest and unclearly expressed needs of the economy and society for research results.

The need for government bodies for science and technology has again been recognised. These were established first in the federal units and more recently at the national level. The current situation is as follows:

- Bosnia-Herzegovina, Republic Committee for Education, Science, Culture and Physical Education,
- Montenegro, Republic Committee for Education, Culture and Science,
- Croatia, Republic Committee for Science, Technology and Computer Science,
- Macedonia, Republic Committee for Science and Technology,
- Slovenia, Republic Committee for Research and Technology,
- Serbia, Republic Committee for Science, Technology and Computer Science,
- Vojvodina, Regional Committee for Science and Computer Science,
- Kosovo, Regional Committee for Education and Science,
- Yugoslavia, Federal Committee for Science and Technology.

In principle, these bodies do not allocate funds for financing R&D. Committees for science and technology are managing boards consisting of representatives of industry, scientific organisations and associations, service sectors, etc. They deal with government policy measures concerning research work, with regulations, science and technology development planning.

Public purchases or government procurement can also be a very powerful institutional tool for technology development. In Yugoslavia, this tool is used by each federal unit and, to a lesser extent – except for military procurements – at the national level. This has had two visible effects. The first is a practically complete independence of federal units in the area of public purchases for their own needs and self-sufficient development of their own capacities for these needs. The second effect, which is almost entirely negative, is a radical decrease of the volume and size of individual public procurements, and in the capability of procurement to finance the domestic development of appropriate technologies and production. The result is an almost complete dependence on the importation of technologies or products for public needs (post and telecommunications, radio and TV networks, railway, part of the electric power system, health services, education, and the Social Accountancy Service which controls socially owned resources, particularly payments). Military production is an exception, and shows that larger public procurements in domestic industry can be a competent and competitive means for developing the capability of domestic institutes and industry thereby meeting local and export needs.

During the last 15 years, political and other public activities concerning science and technology, have passed through two very different phases. In the first, which lasted until the beginning of the 1980s, research was considered merely as a matter of general economic and social reorganisation rather than as an element of active policy for economic and social development. Social reorganisation was directed mainly towards decentralisation. This has increased the activities of research workers and institutes in formulating and negociating projects. However, this interest waned and became shorter-term, with the diminution of the number of projects formulated within the planning framework. Commercialisation of research results improved the capacity for recognising economic needs for research, but since these were modest, the main concern of the research system was to survive. During this phase of decentralisation, numerous research groups emerged within research organisations but they became increasingly uncoordinated and autonomous.

The second phase can be traced back to the economic crisis and the awareness that dependence on foreign technology could not solve this crisis. This led to political action in favour of the development and use of domestic research potential. In this phase, which is continuing, there is a stronger public confidence in domestic research potential and the possibilities of science and technology to solve major problems. This situation is favourable for stimulating science and technology. At the same time it implies greater social risk, since it arises from practical considerations and is not based on a firm political, cultural and general public conviction that economic and social development are largely dependent on the development and use of results of domestic R&D activities. Moreover, doubts remain about the possibility of implementing an efficient science and technology policy at the national level.

1. Development of the research organisations network

The number of research organisations per basic group and field of science in 1970, 1975, and for the period 1980-84, is given in Table 7. This overall picture clearly shows sudden changes which occurred after 1975. These changes are mainly the consequence of internal organisational changes in the existing research organisations, and are only partly due to establishment of new ones. At that time a number of radical changes took place in Yugoslavia.

Table 7. **Numbers of research and development organisations by field of science – 1970-84**

Scientific field	1970	1975	1980	1981	1982	1983	1984
Research organisations, total	261	270	479	484	481	480	469
Natural-mathematical sciences	28	28	59	55	50	52	51
Technical-technological sciences	80	90	216	216	208	207	206
Medical sciences	15	21	31	30	31	35	35
Bio-technical sciences	58	51	61	62	48	64	56
Social sciences	80	80	78	86	84	85	86
Humanities			34	35	40	37	35
Research-development units, total	202	232	88	92	104	102	118
Natural-mathematical sciences	11	9	3	4	8	5	8
Technical-technological sciences	147	153	51	52	56	63	63
Medical sciences	8	11	18	22	23	22	33
Bio-technical sciences	11	20	3	4	6	4	3
Social sciences			7	7	6	5	6
Humanities	25	39	6	3	5	3	5
Scientific units of universities, total[1]	116	151	259	273	269	298	305
Natural-mathematical sciences	5	8	30	32	35	34	33
Technical-technological sciences	42	50	84	88	87	97	100
Medical sciences	13	15	15	35	35	38	40
Bio-technical sciences	13	15	41	45	42	43	43
Social sciences	43	63	47	47	45	55	59
Humanities			22	26	25	31	30
Total: (Research organisations, R&D units, universities)	579	653	826	849	854	880	892
Natural-mathematical sciences	44	45	92	91	93	91	92
Technical-technological sciences	269	293	351	356	357	367	369
Medical sciences	36	47	84	87	89	95	108
Bio-technical sciences	82	86	105	111	96	111	102
Social sciences			132	140	135	145	151
Humanities	148	182	62	64	70	71	70

1. For 1970 and 1975 the total number of faculties is given. For other years the total number of faculty basic organisations of associated labour (BOAL) and the number without BOAL are provided.
Source: See Table 1.

Figure 2. NUMBER OF RESEARCH WORKERS IN YUGOSLAVIA

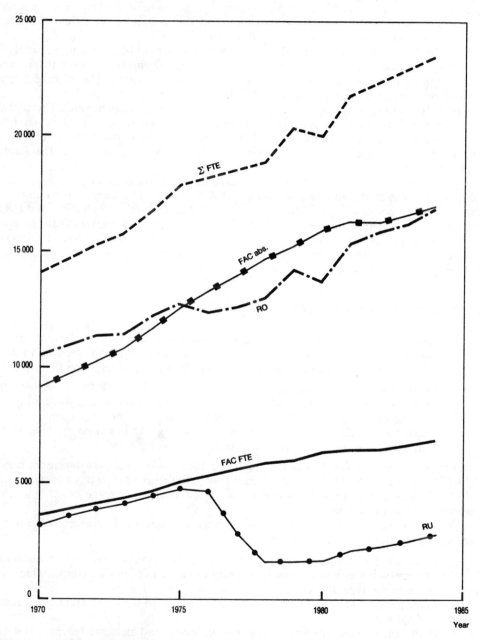

FAC FTE = full-time equivalant faculty;
FAC abs. = faculty in absolute numbers;
RO   = research organisations;
RU   = research and development units.

33

The reorganisation of enterprises and institutions in all fields led to the establishment of basic organisations of associated labour (BOAL) especially in larger organisations, and large enterprises were transformed into complex organisations of associated labour. These changes were much more obvious in research institutes, and less at universities (where there is a stronger traditional internal close-knit organisation).

Establishment of basic organisations of associated labor (BOAL) took place mostly in the field of technical and natural sciences, and primarily in large institutes. Since BOAL took over all functions, statistical data and indicators were also changed. The average size of research organisations was significantly reduced.

In this period a sudden decrease in the number of research units can be noted. Until 1975, these were mostly research and development centres within industrial organisations. After the changes mentioned above, all important R&D centres having the status of "basic" or "work" organisation were transferred to the group of research organisations, i.e. to the former independent institutes.

This statistical classification explains the discontinuity in the time series, and especially the disappearance of the autonomous group of R&D centres. The trend in the number of research workers per basic organisation group (universities, research organisations and R&D units) is shown in Figure 2. The graph showing the number of research workers, in the group of R&D units, indicates the process described above. The research organisations' (RO) curve includes the total number of individual institutes and research units. The organisational continuity of the universities is also evident.

2. Employment and structure of research staff

The survey of the number of R&D units, number of researchers, average size of organisation and the change of the number of research workers per field of science (Table 8) and a parallel survey of the same indicators for faculties (Table 9) show the following:

- There was a 27 per cent increase in the total number of R&D units over the period 1970-84, while the number of research workers employed in these organisations increased by 61 per cent, i.e. an annual growth rate of 3.4 per cent.
- Simultaneously the number of faculties and teaching staff increased by about 84 per cent, with an average annual growth rate of 4.5 per cent.

The number of teaching staff and associates per faculty did not change during the period 1970-84 (an average of 80 professors per faculty), while in the group of research organisations and R&D units the number of employees increased from an average of 22.5 to 28.6 researchers per organisation.

When measured by the number of research workers, there are differences in the size of research organisation by field of science:

- In the group of independent institutes, the largest organisations are in natural and technical sciences, while the smallest are in social sciences and humanities which is in line with the type of research, i.e., the size of "critical masses".
- In the group of R&D units, the largest units are in the technical, technological and medical sciences.
- In the universities, the biggest group of professors and associate teachers is in the medical faculties where teaching largely takes place in specialised clinical hospitals. The next biggest group is in the natural sciences and mathematical faculties, where there is a wide span of scientific disciplines.

In the period 1970-84, the main changes in the relative share of researchers by field of science, and by group of research and development organisations, are the following:

- In the group of institutes and R&D units (Table 8), the share of agricultural sciences decreased significantly, that of natural and technical sciences somewhat less, while the share of medical, social sciences and humanities significantly increased.
- In the group of faculties, the share of social sciences and humanities, and to a lesser extent, that of natural sciences increased; the share of technical sciences stagnated; and the share of medical and agricultural sciences decreased.

Table 8. **Independent institutes and R&D units by field of science – 1970-84**

	Organi-sations[1]	Total	Natural, mathe-matical	Technical & technological	Medical	Agricultural	Social & humanities
Number of organisations							
1970	RO	261	28	80	15	58	80
	RU	202	11	147	8	11	25
1981	RO	484	55	216	30	62	121
	RU	92	4	52	22	4	10
1984	RO	469	51	206	35	56	121
	RU	118	8	63	33	3	11
Number of researchers							
1970	RO	7 120	1 269	3 009	433	1 142	1 267
	RU	3 323	70	2 860	34	234	125
1981	RO	13 438	1 627	7 288	866	1 209	2 446
	RU	2 027	80	1 335	495	15	138
1984	RO	14 145	1 867	7 531	947	1 416	2 375
	RU	2 633	117	1 620	706	16	174
Average size of organisation							
(number of researchers per organisation)							
1970	RO	27.3	45.3	37.6	28.9	19.7	15.8
	RU	16.5	6.4	19.5	4.2	21.3	5.0
1981	RO	27.8	29.6	33.7	28.9	19.5	19.6
	RU	22.0	20.0	25.7	20.9	3.7	15.8
1984	RO	30.2	36.8	36.6	27.1	25.3	19.6
	RU	22.3	14.6	25.7	21.4	5.3	15.8
Changes in the share of researchers							
per field of science (per cent)							
1970	RO+RU	100.0	12.8	56.2	4.5	13.2	13.3
1981	RO+RU	100.0	11.0	55.8	8.6	7.9	16.7
1984	RO+RU	100.0	11.9	54.5	9.8	8.5	15.2

1. RO = research organisations, RU = research and development units.
Source: See Table 1.

The level of education of research and development personnel by groups of research organisations in 1981 varies greatly. The data presented in Table 10 lead to the following remarks:

- The level of education of the personnel in research organisations, including the R&D units, differs widely from that of the university teaching staff. In the former, 13.5 per cent of personnel have a PhD degree (15.5 per cent in the institutes only) as against 40.8 per cent in the faculties. In the case of persons with Masters' degrees, the difference is much smaller, 13.7 per cent of the total in research organisations and 21.5 per cent in the faculties.

Table 9. **Tertiary level education – 1970-84**

	University level organisations, total	Field of science				
		Natural & mathematical	Technical & technological	Medical	Agricultural	Social & humanities
Number of faculties						
1970-71	116	5	42	13	13	43
1975-76	151	8	50	15	15	63
1980-81	209	13	80	20	16	80
1984-85	214	13	81	20	18	82
Number of professors and associates						
1970-71	9 354	662	3 011	2 057	1 204	2 420
1975-76	10 999	984	3 472	2 341	1 267	2 935
1980-81	15 990	1 511	4 765	3 441	1 702	4 571
1984-85	17 205	1 647	5 579	3 169	1 775	5 035
Average size of the faculty (number of professors and associates per faculty)						
1970-71	80.6	132.4	71.7	158.2	92.6	56.3
1975-76	72.8	132.0	69.4	156.1	84.5	46.6
1980-81	76.5	116.2	59.6	172.1	106.4	57.1
1984-85	80.4	126.7	68.9	158.5	98.6	61.4
Changes in the share of the number of professors and associates per field of science (per cent)						
1970-71	100.0	7.1	32.3	22.0	12.9	25.9
1975-76	100.0	8.9	31.6	21.3	11.5	26.7
1980-81	100.0	9.4	29.8	21.5	10.6	28.6
1984-85	100.0	9.6	32.4	18.4	10.3	29.3

Source: See Table 1.

Table 10. **Level of education of research staff – 1981**

Type of research organisation	Researchers			Expert and technical staff			Total		
	Total	PhD	MSc	Total	PhD	MSc	Total	PhD	MSc
Research organisations (RO)	11 541	1 885	1 878	1 775	11	28	13 316	1 996	1 906
Research and development units (RU)	1 777	179	206	250	–	3	2 027	179	209
RO + RU	13 318	2 064	2 084	2 025	11	31	15 343	2 075	2 115
Faculties	11 443	5 758	2 434	3 248	237	720	14 691	5 995	3 154
Total (RO + RU + Faculties)	24 761	7 822	4 518	5 273	248	751	30 034	8 070	5 269

Source: See Table 1.

- Data on relocation of the R&D staff show a low mobility and a "one-way street" mentality prevailing in research careers. Personnel come from industry, pass through institutes and finish their careers in the faculties. The major part of the teaching staff is recruited from students and post-graduates, i.e. at the faculty itself.
- Out of the total number of persons with a PhD degree working in research, three fourths (74.3 per cent) are in university faculties. This reflects the strict regulations in education, and the more convenient conditions for the preparation of a doctoral thesis available to staff employed in the universities.

- Significant differences also exist between individual fields of science, conditioned by the process of acquiring a PhD degree in certain fields.
- The proportion of MSc graduates has gradually increased as a result of the expansion of post-graduate studies, i.e. as a result of the great importance of formal conditions for career advancement in research in general, and more especially in university faculties.

According to 1974 and 1981 censuses, persons possessing a PhD degree were employed as follows (Table 11):

- In 1981 only 6.2 per cent of persons with a PhD degree were employed in industry, and 93.8 per cent in non-industrial activities. This is typical for countries with a technologically underdeveloped economy.
- The number of persons possessing a PhD degree employed in the industry, mining and agriculture decreased . This indicates that the economic climate is not favourable to researchers with a PhD degree.
- Education absorbs the majority of PhDs (60.5 per cent in 1981) with a tendency to increase its share despite lower personal income in education than in industry. This indicates that the conditions for research work of PhDs are more better in education than in industry.
- There are limited possibilities for increasing the number of research workers. The growth rate of 4.5 per cent annually is mostly the result of persons already employed in research and acquiring a PhD degree.
- The most rapid growth of the number of PhDs is in medical sciences (13.2 per cent annually).

Table 11. **Employment of PhD degree graduates by field of work**

Year	Total	Industry	Non-industry	Field of work							
				Industry & mining	Agri-culture	Education & culture		Research and development		Health & social security	SPC and SPO[1]
						Number	%	Number	%		
1974	6 713	468	6 245	223	124	3 944	58.8	1 336	19.9	538	428
1981	10 769	665	10 104	206	96	6 516	60.5	1 825	16.9	1 282	426
Growth rate (per cent)	7.0	5.2	7.1	−1.1	−3.7	7.4		4.5		13.2	0

1. SPC = Socio-political communities; SPO = Socio-political organisations
Source: See Table 1.

3. University education: financing and output of graduates

In real terms total expenditure for university education (Table 12) decreased quite sharply (by about 30 per cent) in the period 1980-84, as a result of restrictions on total expenditure for "non-production" sectors of the economy. The share in GDP devoted to university education fell from 0.74 per cent in 1980 to 0.52 per cent in 1984.

Table 12. **University expenditure and sources of income – 1980-84**

	1980	1981	1982	1983	1984
Total expenditure in university education (million dinars)	11 479	14 861	18 521	22 967	33 045
Share of university education funds in GDP (per cent)	0.74	0.67	0.63	0.56	0.52
University education funds per student (thousand dinars)	35.4	49.6	61.3	78.4	118.8
University education funds, by source (million dinars):					
SCIs for university education	6 469	8 513	9 936	11 661	18 880
Percentage share	56.4	57.3	53.6	50.8	57.1
SCIs for science	719	1 156	1 776	2 424	3 126
Percentage share	6.3	7.8	9.6	10.6	9.5
Industry	3 426	4 143	5 466	6 741	8 487
Percentage share	29.8	27.9	29.5	29.3	25.7
Other sources	865	1 049	1 343	2 141	2 552
Percentage share	7.5	7.0	7.3	9.3	7.7

Source: See Table 1.

Self-management communities of interest (SCI) for education and the industry provide the largest share of university funds (50-57 per cent and 26-30 per cent, respectively). The SCI for science provide 6-10 per cent. Industry directly finances some educational, research, project planning, consulting and other activities carried out by the universities.

The funds per student are not sufficient to ensure the necessary standard of university education, especially in the natural and technical sciences. University education experienced an explosive development during the 40 years from 1945 to 85. Some 570 286 graduates were produced in this period.

In some years up to 30 000 students graduated, i.e. 25 per 10 000 of the active population. However, the number of graduates in technical sciences is small, both relatively and in absolute terms, amounting to only 3 graduates per 1 000 employed in the industry (Table 13).

In the period 1945-85, the proportion of social sciences and humanities graduates was particularly high (48.3 per cent: including 36 per cent social sciences, dominated by economics). This distribution is unsatisfactory in relation to the employment possibilities of university graduates, and is even worse in relation to the needs of rapid technological development.

The trends in acquisition of PhD degrees have been the following (Table 14):

- The sudden surge of PhD graduates in 1964-65 was a reaction to more demanding requirements for acquiring a PhD degree, effective from the beginning of 1966. This subsequently resulted in a "low-tide" with long-lasting consequences.
- The growth rate of the number of PhDs significantly increased after 1972 when responsibility for the formulation of requirements for acquiring a PhD degree passed from the federation to the republics with simultaneous expansion of faculties.

Acquisition of a PhD degree differs from one field of science to another (Table 14). Of particular interest is the period 1966-81. In this period the highest growth rate was achieved by the technical sciences (19.2 per cent) followed by medical (14.5 per cent) and social sciences (14.3 per cent). However, the high growth rate in the number of PhD degrees in the technical sciences seems to reflect the low base (i.e. a small number of PhDs) in 1966.

Table 13. **Students and graduates by field of science**

	1945-85 Number	1945-85 %	1980	1981	1982	1983	1984	1985
Graduated students	570 286	100.0	30 091	30 703	31 494	30 867	29 551	27939
Natural sciences	36 254	6.4	1 829	1 488	1 487	1 702	1 420	1 339
Technical & technological sciences	135 965	23.8	6 560	7 025	7 169	6 879	6 664	6 125
Medical sciences	78 681	13.8	3 591	3 356	3 930	3 500	3 410	3 740
Bio-technical sciences	1 421	7.7	1 669	1 727	1 886	1 886	1 879	1 694
Social sciences	205 647	36.1	13 200	13 592	14 106	13 828	13 507	12 389
Cultural-historical sciences	69 557	12.2	3 490	3 573	3 075	3 072	2 671	2 652
Number of students per 10 000 population	–	–	145.5	133.4	133.4	128.5	121.1	
Number of graduates per 10 000 active population	–	–	24.6	24.9	25.4	24.7	23.5	
Number of graduates of technical sciences per 1 000 employed in industry	–	–	3.0	3.1	3.1	2.9	2.7	
Total Faculties	–	–	206	209	213	215	211	
Students	–	–	324 453	299 724	302 109	292 985	278 057	

Source: See Table 1.

Table 14. **PhD degrees awarded by field of science**

Field of science	Total number of PhD awarded in the period 1945-82 Number	Total number of PhD awarded in the period 1945-82 Participation	Participation in the period (per cent) 1945-60	Participation in the period (per cent) 1961-70	Participation in the period (per cent) 1971-82	Average annual growth rate in the period (percent) 1966-81	Average annual growth rate in the period (percent) 1975-81
Natural & mathematical sciences	2 764	21.1	25.0	25.6	18.3	10.8	7.0
Technical & technological sciences	1 774	13.5	8.4	8.8	16.5	19.2	13.4
Bio-technical sciences	1 999	15.2	25.7	20.2	11.1	12.3	7.7
Medical sciences	2 723	20.7	8.4	13.6	26.2	14.5	4.7
Social and human sciences	3 868	29.5	32.5	31.8	27.9	25.4	13.5
Total	13 127	100.0	100.0	100.0	100.0	13.9	7.8

Source: See Table 1.

More recent growth rates during the period 1975-81 show a general slowing down in the output of PhDs. While technical and social sciences are still leading, the growth in medical sciences has slowed as a result of relative saturation, i.e. diminution of potential candidates (slower growth of teaching staff at faculties and research workers in institutes).

Over the period 1945-81, the ratio of the number of new PhDs to the number of graduates remained almost constant. During this period, a PhD degree was acquired by 26.2 in every 1 000 graduates (27.5 persons in every 1 000 graduates in the period 1970-81). The number of new MScs was also stable at around 60 per thousand graduates.

Figure 3. **SHARE OF R&D FUNDS AS PERCENTAGE OF NATIONAL INCOME: YUGOSLAVIA AND FEDERAL UNITS**

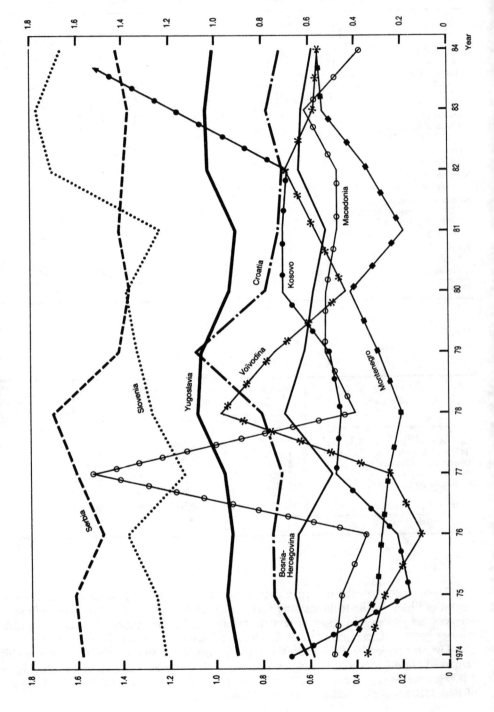

4. Research and development expenditure

For many years, R&D expenditures have oscillated within a narrow range from 0.91 per cent to 1.08 per cent of domestic product using the Yugoslav definition (i.e. from 0.82 per cent to 0.97 per cent of GDP as defined by OECD). Between the six republics and two provinces there are considerable differences in the level of expenditures and intensity of fluctuations (Figure 3). The relative magnitude of R&D expenditures reflects the level of economic development of the various federal units. The exceptions are Serbia, which spends more than the national average (when it would be expected to be closer to the average by the criterion of industrial development), and Croatia which invests less in R&D than the national average and should be somewhat higher. The explanation for Serbia can be found in the concentration of research organisations, especially in Belgrade where the so-called "federal institutes" were established during the 1950s and 1960s.

Although the level of R&D expenditures has recently stagnated, the current objective is to double it in real terms. The last three five-year plans (1971-85), as well as the current development plan for the period 1986-90, explicitly set the goal of investment in R&D at 2 per cent of the national income. This has not yet been achieved because there is no efficient self-management mechanism which can ensure the attainment of such a goal. Moreover, cyclical restrictions of investments are reflected directly in the allocation of R&D funds in the area of Self-management Communities of Interest for Science (SCIS).

Research organisations receive income from two main sources: funds for R&D, and the income earned by selling expert services and products. The ratio between the two sources is 70 per cent to 30 per cent, i.e. on average research organisations obtain one third of their income from selling expert services such as analyses, expertise, design, engineering, etc. as well from selling small series and single products. Research activities themselves are financed from two main sources: industry funds, and SCIS funds.

About three fourths of total funds provided by industry are spent in independent institutes, about 12 per cent at faculties and 12 per cent in R&D units. However, the only reliable figure relates to universities, since the distinction made from 1977 onwards between research organisations and R&D units, gives a very distorted picture. Research organisations also include industrial R&D centres with the status of basic organisation of labour, while about 40 per cent of the group of R&D units are in the field of social and medical sciences.

SCIS funds provide, on an average, 20 per cent of resources of research organisations. Besides SCI for Science, specific research activities are financed by SCI for other activities (e.g. health, education, etc.) as well as governmental agencies. These SCI provide about 10 per cent of total R&D funds.

The total R&D funds of republic and regional SCIS are gradually decreasing as a result of restrictions introduced since 1979. This trend in the two main sources of R&D funding is accompanied by negative effects: low employment and sub-critical investment in equipment and facilities. The SCIS provide between 26.3 and 33.0 per cent of science faculty funds, between 1.8 and 7.2 per cent of R&D unit funds and between 62.8 and 70.1 per cent of research organisation funds.

Other sources of R&D funds are receipts from non-industrial organisations which commissioned studies, and receipts from patents and licences. Funds from foreign sources are relatively small: in the period 1980-84, they amounted to between 1.1 to 2.7 per cent of total R&D expenditures. These funds include receipts from research work on projects within special programmes (such as the Yugoslav-American Fund) and from projects conducted by research organisations for developing countries.

41

Figure 4. **R&D FUNDS AS A PERCENTAGE OF NATIONAL INCOME**

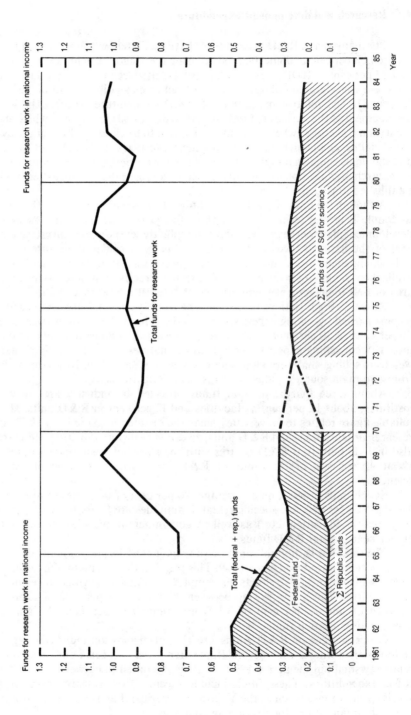

Under the 1986-90 plan SCIS funds are set to rise so that their share would reach at least one third of the total R&D funds. In addition, in order to support big strategic projects on a national level, it is planned to establish a federal fund for technological development.

This fund will support two types of projects:

- projects performed by consortia of industrial and research organisations from several republics and provinces, with a view to integrating Yugoslav resources and efforts; and
- international co-operation projects with foreign partners in which a group of organisations from several republics and provinces participates on behalf of Yugoslavia (the objective being to enable these organisations to deal on equal terms with foreign partners).

5. Research and development by category of research

Yugoslav statistics record completed research projects as a measure of R&D activities. Research projects are classified by research organisations in one of three categories: fundamental, applied, or development. Each category includes projects which are significantly different in size, in time-scale and in funds invested, etc. In spite of this, it is possible to use these statistics to follow trends in the main categories of research.

In the period 1978-84, fundamental research projects remained a relatively constant fraction of total research – between 15 and 20 per cent. This is in line with countries of similar size and level of development. However, because of insufficient investment since the early 1970s, equipment for basic research has been wholly inadequate and obsolete. This leads to the conclusion that Yugoslavia is gradually lagging behind in fundamental research – as measured by its place in world scientific literature. With regard to performers of fundamental research, the universities account for the most important share with 25 to 30 per cent of research projects in this category; institutes account for around 15 per cent and R&D units account for 5 per cent.

The distribution of activities between applied research and development differs from the situation in industrialised countries. This was especially true in the period 1978-81 when applied research projects amounted to 60 per cent of total research, while development projects amounted to only 25 per cent. After 1981, the situation improved quite markedly and the development category reached 38 per cent in 1984. This probably results from the decreased possibility of import of technologies from industrialised countries after 1980; industry reduced its purchases of foreign licences and developed more of its own technology. The technical sciences account for almost one half of the total number of research projects categorised as development.

IV. THE RESEARCH ORGANISATIONS

1. Free exchange of labour

The Constitution of Yugoslavia stipulates the principle of free exchange of labour as the basis of relationships between the producers of services and the users of their results. In the field of research these relationships are determined by means of medium-term plans of socio-political communities: organisations of associated labour, and Self-Management Communities of Interest (SCI) for Science. Annual plans define the details of the medium-term plans and also determine the funds necessary for realisation of programmes based on self-management decisions. These funds, including the salaries of employees, come from annually determined contributions of organisations of associated labour. Part of the funding is provided under agreements with certain industrial sectors, groups of organisations of associated labour or major industrial entreprises, whose interest in realisation of research programmes is "above average".

Success in realising the plans referred to above is evaluated by the delegates of the SCI, by scientific experts and also by workers associated with the SCI. This is done each year in the context of preparation of the next annual plan.

Direct exchange of labour is governed by long-term self-management agreements and contracts between research organisations and users of research results. This free exchange of labour constitutes about 60-70 per cent of total R & D funds. Agreements and contracts can be connected with programmes and projects in the area of the SCI for Science.

The connection between research programmes financed in the area of the SCI for Science and projects directly negotiated with industrial organisations is not strong. This tends to reduce the contribution of research work to technological development.

2. Independent research and development institutes

The basic network of research organisations (RO) was formed in the first decade of postwar reconstruction; an average of 8.5 scientific institutes and 3.3 developmental units were established yearly. In this period the academies of science established 30 scientific institutions, mostly in the field of natural, social sciences and the humanities, while government agencies established 24 institutes linked to economic activities such as industry, mining and construction.

During the period 1960-64 over 20 institutes per year were established and the growth rate of research workers reached 10 per cent per year. In this same period, federal and republic councils were created and funds for scientific work were established, stimulating the extension of the research organisations network. After 1965, the rate of creation of independent institutes decreased to about 4 per year. The establishment of a large number of institutes, most of them being very small and having overlapping research activities, is due to several causes:

- Since Yugoslavia is a multi-national country it was necessary to meet both national and regional needs, which are different;
- The Academies of Sciences tended to promote their own scientific institutions, especially in the field of fundamental research and in humanities; and
- Universities established their own independent institutes, since funds for scientific work encouraged more research in institutes than at universities. Leading researchers worked in these institutes, while faculty laboratories remained underdeveloped, and below the critical threshold.

As already noted, after 1979 all R&D units within industrial organisations with the status of "basic" or "work" organisation were transferred to the category of research organisations, i.e. the former independent institutes. This almost doubled the number of research organisations (from 270 in 1975 to about 480 in 1980). This decentralisation stimulated interest in development problems and increased staff motivation for more creative and productive work. However, it also had several negative side effects:

- Basic organisations of associated labour (BOAL) gained full autonomy, so that connections between different BOAL in complex institutes were very loose and the R&D programmes of institutes became often a mere collection of individual programmes of BOAL;
- Since BOAL were formed without the implementation of specific criteria to ensure critical masses of research resources (personnel, equipment and funds), very small organisations resulted which lost their R&D purpose and in some cases were subsequently transformed into design or service groups.

In order to counter these trends, laws and procedures were adopted:

- Imposing minimum conditions on BOAL: the number of research workers, their qualifications (number of PhD and Masters degrees), working premises, equipment and information-documentation base; and
- Strengthening the common functions of the BOAL especially in the field of development and investment planning.

For example, the law regarding research activities, enacted by Serbia proper (Serbia without the autonomous provinces) in 1984, stipulated the minimum number of research workers at 20, including 5 PhDs and 5 Masters degrees testifying to appropriate scientific training. These measures led to a gradual decrease of the number of organisations in 1984-85.

The number of research workers employed in independent institutes comprised 51.4 per cent of the total number of FTE research staff in 1970, 45.4 per cent in 1975, and an estimated 50 per cent in 1984-85. Of the remainder, about 20 per cent are employed in R&D units in industrial organisations of associated labour and 30 per cent are employed in the universities.

Analysis of the use of R&D personnel is based on the income structure of research organisations (Table 15). The only concentrated source of funds is the SCI for Science (eight republic and regional SCIs). Other sources are divided among numerous organisations, as can be seen latter from the number of the so called "completed R&D works", which amount to more than 20 000 per year.

Most of the research work of the independent institutes is in the scientific services area where the average project (contract) is relatively small. In 1985, the total revenue from

Table 15. **Sources of funds and participation of research organisations in R&D performance**

	1980 A(D)	1980 P(%)	1981 A(D)	1981 P(%)	1982 A(D)	1982 P(%)	1983 A(D)	1983 P(%)	1984 A(D)	1984 P(%)
SCI for science	2 405	18.2	3 501	19.2	5 716	21.3	8 500	22.8	11 900	20.8
Other SCI	845	6.4	1 315	7.2	1 686	6.3	1 838	4.9	3 034	5.3
Socio-political	930	7.0	983	5.4	1 156	4.3	1 458	3.9	2 251	3.9
Industry	7 244	56.2	10 421	57.1	14 697	54.7	20 764	55.6	32 116	56.2
Foreign	152	1.2	333	1.8	332	1.2	641	1.7	1 522	2.7
Other funds	1 460	11.0	1 689	9.3	3 293	12.3	4 133	11.1	6 282	11.0
Total	13 214	100.0	18 242	100.0	26 880	100.0	37 334	100.0	57 105	100.0

A = Amount
P = Participation
Source: See Table 1.

Table 16. **R&D funds by performing institution – 1984**
Per cent

	Total	SCI for Science	Other SCI	Socio-political	Industry	Foreign	Other funds
RO	71.2	70.1	43.8	83.6	76.4	83.2	53.1
RU	11.0	3.6	5.6	10.3	11.9	1.2	25.2
Faculties	17.8	26.3	50.6	6.1	11.7	15.6	21.7
Total	100.0	100.0	100.0	100.0	100.0	100.0	100.0

Source: See Table 1.

Table 17 **R&D expenditure by groups of research organisations – 1984**
Per cent

	Total	SCI for Science	Other SCI	Socio-political	Industry	Foreign	Other funds
RO	100.0	20.5	3.3	4.6	60.3	3.1	8.2
RU	100.0	6.9	2.7	3.7	61.1	0.3	25.3
Faculties	100.0	30.7	15.1	1.4	37.1	2.3	13.4

Source: See Table 1.

Table 18. **Trends in R&D funding and expenditure – 1980-84**

		1980	1981	1982	1983	1984
National[1]	Funding	31.6	31.8	31.9	31.6	30.0
	Expenditure	76.8	75.5	71.0	69.5	71.2
University education	Funding	–	–	–	–	–
	Expenditure	17.9	18.9	18.4	18.4	17.9
Industry	Funding	56.2	57.1	54.7	55.6	56.2
	Expenditure	6.3	5.6	10.6	12.1	10.9
Other	Funding	12.2	11.1	13.5	12.8	13.7
	Expenditure	na	na	na	na	na

1. These are public funds, and the R&D performing organisations are the Independent Institutes.
na = data not available.
Source: See Table 1.

research work of all research organisations amounted to 68 778.2 million dinars, and completed R&D works to 16 085 million dinars. The average size of a project was 4.276 million dinars.

In order to modify the presently unsatisfactory ratio between the personnel employed by independent institutes and those employed in R&D centres in industry, two measures are planned:

- Investing funds to boost the number of research workers in R&D centres (especially by stimulating the entry and training of young research workers); and
- Entrusting specialised independent institutes with R&D functions in appropriate industrial organisations.

The technical facilities of independent institutes are much weaker than those of R&D centres in industry. This is particularly reflected in the value of equipment per employee which amounts to 60 per cent of that in industry. There are important differences between scientific fields.

The natural and physical sciences are the best equipped technically, reflecting the experimental nature of their research. However, this area also has the highest degree of obsolete equipment, so that the present value is about 20 per cent of the purchase value. Consequently there is a lag in the development of basic research in physics, chemistry and biology and a weakening of the base for applied research and development.

In regard to equipment, facilities for technological sciences generally lag behind those of industry. The institutes tend to be more involved in such activities as design, technical-economic and feasibility studies than in the development of new technologies. This explains why the value of technical facilities per employee is only 70 per cent of the comparable figure for industry, and the present value of equipment is 35 per cent of the purchase value. In bio-technical sciences the equipment value per employee is about 50 per cent that of industry.

3. University research organisations and units

University education in Yugoslavia has undergone rapid growth in recent years in response to increasing needs for highly educated personnel. Three universities existed in 1945 and two new ones were established in 1960. A "Resolution" on university education was enacted by the National Assembly in 1960. Ten new universities were created in republic and regional centres over the period 1960-80. According to the Yugoslav classification in the academic year 1984-85 there were, within the 20 universities, some 214 faculties and colleges and 303 university research organisations and units.

The primary role of these organisations is educational, with research as a second function. Faculties and colleges are mostly organised along classical lines, in departments, divisions and laboratories. Each faculty is considered as one research organisation. If the faculty has basic organisations of associated labour, then each of these organisations is counted as a "university research organisation and unit". Faculties may also comprise several research institutes.

The universities in Yugoslavia are associations of faculties, colleges and independent institutes which have to satisfy certain criteria in order to become members of universities. Internal connections between members of universities are generally weak, especially in the field of education programmes and joint research projects. The role and place of independent institutes within the universities is particularly ill-defined, because even though they can carry

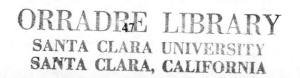

Table 19. **Trends in university organisation**

	1984-85	1983-84	1982-83	1981-82	1980-81
Faculties and Colleges	214	215	215	217	213
University Research Organisations and units	303	306	298	269	273

Source: Statistical Yearbook of Yugoslavia.

out post-graduate studies according to the law, they do so only to a limited extent and almost exclusively in association with a university faculty.

Expressed in FTE, university personnel undertaking R&D activities increased from 25.8 per cent of the total number of FTE research workers in 1970 to 31.9 per cent in 1980. This growth was followed by a relative stagnation, as a result of strict restrictions on the growth of the universities, limitation of student enrolments and, from 1980, a slowing down in the growth of the teaching staff. In 1984, the share of university professors and associates amounted, in FTE, to 28.8 per cent. R&D personnel in faculties amounted to one half of the total number of research workers. In terms of pattern of qualifications, the faculties are by far the strongest group of research organisations. The faculties' researchers share of total research workers is an indicator of this, as are the funds invested in research work in faculties compared to the total amount of research funds (Table 20).

Table 20. **University research personnel**
Per cent

Faculties' share	1984	1983	1982	1981	1980
Number of FTE research workers of the faculties in the total number of research workers	28.8	29.9	28.9	29.8	31.9
The share of faculties income from research work in the total funds for research work	17.9	18.9	18.4	18.4	17.9

Source: Statistical Yearbook of Yugoslavia.

This shows that the existing personnel potential of the faculties is used less than the average for all institutions. However, it is necessary to take into account that the category "income from research work" contains only income directly connected with projects performed by faculties for the SCI for Science, for industrial organisations of associated labour and for other external customers. Income from the SCI for Education is attributed entirely to education even though part of these funds is used for training the staff for research.

Separate financing of education and research has brought about a continuous decrease of education funds – both for salaries and investments in equipment. Increased involvement of faculties in research activities and increases in earned income have not been sufficient to compensate for a continuous decrease of funds earmarked for education. In 1984, real income (in fixed prices) of university organisations, for both teaching and research activities, amounted to only 72.4 per cent of 1980 income. At the same time, in current prices, the total income of university faculties increased 2.88 times and the income from research activities increased more than 4.3 times.

It should be noted that the universities' share of total income from direct co-operation with organisations of associated labour in industry for 1984 was almost the double that for 1970. This reflects the effort of the universities to direct their research and education programmes toward the immediate needs of industry and of social, economic and technological development.

The low level of R&D activity in industry constitutes one of the basic difficulties limiting wider involvement of universities in research of direct interest to industry, and in technological development. This is also one of the main reasons why the direct influence of the universities on regional development is relatively limited.

Another important reason concerns a very slow training of staff, particularly in the case of new universities and faculties. The inadequate pattern of qualified scientists and their regional distribution, together with a total lack of mobility of scientific personnel, considerably hinders and slows down the advancement of personnel in universities.

4. Industrial research and development organisations

The economic sector (90 per cent of which is industry) represents the source of more than 55 per cent of total R&D expenditure but it spends only 10-15 per cent of this total on internal R&D. This shows that the situation of R&D in industry is not satisfactory. About 18 per cent of industry employees have a university degree. Out of the total number of PhDs and MScs only 6.3 per cent are employed in industry.

Creation of R&D units (RDU) in industry started immediately after World War II. However, in numbers and size, the development of RDU lagged behind the development of faculties and independent institutes. Until the 1960s, only about 40 RDU were created. Switching from a strictly planned to a market-planned economy accelerated the creation of RDU. Some 77 RDU were established during 1960-64 and 76 more during the period 1965-71. The Law of associated labour in 1976 led to sweeping transformations in the economy, bringing about a sudden decrease of the number of RDU in industry, to less than 80.

Since 1980, all republics and provinces have enacted new laws on research activities which determine the conditions for registration of research organisations. For RDU, these conditions require a smaller number of research workers (i.e. PhDs and MScs) than in the case of creation of independent institutes. However, even under such modest conditions, the number of registered RDU is about 30 and the number of those not satisfying the conditions is 35-40. To this should be added large institutes or complex organisations (about 25) which are registered under the same conditions as independent institutes.

The genesis of RDU is very similar in all industrial entreprises. It usually starts with quality control groups, engineering bureaux or groups responsible for the introduction of products based on foreign licences. Some RDU were established in co-operation with independent institutes when certain research groups moved into industry during the transfer of the results of their research.

Most RDU employ less than 25 research workers. Some industrial institutes, mostly in the field of electrical engineering, chemistry (pharmacy) and metallurgy, have over 50 research workers. In terms of organisation, the majority of RDU are units within "common services" of "complex organisations of associated labour" and some have the status of "basic" or "work" organisation. RDU with the status of basic organisation of associated labour or work organisations are more occupied with research work for new products and technologies, whereas RDU in common services deal mainly with improvement of products and processes in current production programmes.

The work of industrial research units is financed directly by industry (70-75 per cent), by other sources (17-20 per cent) and by SCI (about 10 per cent).

Regulations and current economic measures stimulate creation and development of RDU mainly by exempting industrial organisations from the payment of allowances and income tax on investments in their own research units, by exemption from custom duties for imported equipment, raw materials and semi-finished goods used in R&D, and by other somewhat less important measures.

Yugoslav R&D statistics do not allow for a direct and reliable identification of industrial R&D expenditures, either globally or by sector. On the basis of available data, it can be concluded that industry investment in R&D amount to only about 1.1 per cent of industrial domestic product. Total R&D expenditure for the needs of industry amounts to about 1.3 per cent of industrial domestic product.

Total R&D funds amount to only 3.3 per cent of total investments. R&D funds for industry amount to only 2.6 per cent of total investments of industry, while industrial R&D is only 5 per cent of total investments of industry. This is the consequence of a global development philosophy and policy based, almost exclusively, on the procurement of traditional factors of production and based on marginalisation of the importance of science and technology for production and development.

The relative increase of R&D funds in total investments which occurred in the period 1980-85 reflects only a decrease in other investments, since the level of R&D funds remained almost stable.

Of all employees with a university education, 54 per cent work in non-industrial sectors and only 18 per cent in industry (Table 21). In 1983, employees with university education represented 6.9 per cent of the total number of employees, 22.1 per cent in non-industrial sectors and 3.4 per cent in industry. The total number of PhD and MSc graduates is high – about 25 000. Most are employed in non-industrial sectors (about 84 per cent) and only 6.5 per cent in industry. There are thus only 0.7 potential research workers with postgraduate degree per 1 000 employees in industry.

Relatively modest R&D expenditure, low internal R&D effort and a very small number of research workers indicate that industry lacks an appropriate R&D infrastructure for intensive innovation. Most R&D potential is situated outside industry. Furthermore, weak relations between this R&D potential and industry is one of the reasons for its low effectiveness and efficiency.

Table 21. **Numbers of public sector employees by main sectors**

Thousands

Sectors of employment	1980 Total	1981 Total	1981 UE[1] Total	1981 UE[1] D+M	1981 HSW	1981 SSE	1982 Total	1983 Total	1983 UE[1] Total	1983 UE[1] D+M	1983 HSW	1983 SSE	1984 Total	1985 Total
Economy	4 826	4 968	175.2	3.7			5 079	5 178	201	4.4			5 293	5 432
Non-industry	972	998	212.5	19.5			1 025	1 045	231	20.5			1 062	1 084
Industry	2 162	2 242	69.2	1.4	136	275	2 313	2 374	81	1.7	135	323	2 445	2 529
Total	5 798	5 966	387.7	23.2			6 104	6 222	432	24.9			6 355	6 516

1. UE = University Education, SSE = Secondary school education, HSW = Highly skilled worker, D+M = Doctorate and Masters graduates.
Source: Statistical Yearbook of Yugoslavia.

5. Council of Academies of Science and Art of Yugoslavia

The Council of Academies of Science and Art of Yugoslavia is the co-ordinating body of Academies of Science and Art of all federal units, with the following tasks:
- studying general questions of science and cultural policy, as well as other general questions of common interest;
- exchanging experiences between the academies and encouraging their co-operation;
- initiating, and co-ordinating scientific and other joint activities of the academies;
- co-operating with federal bodies for science and culture in formulating scientific and cultural policy and in realising research programmes;
- organising joint publications between the academies;
- establishing inter-academies boards and joint activities with other scientific and artistic bodies;
- representing the academies in Yugoslavia and abroad;
- managing common funds of the academies; and
- carrying out other activities and tasks of common interest entrusted to the academies.

The Council's headquarters moves every three years according to an agreed order. Creation of academies in certain federal units has been a long-term process. First, scientific associations were formed among universities and, after a period of time, academies were established.

The oldest academy is the Yugoslav Academy of Science and Arts, established in 1861 with its main office in Zagreb. The Serbian Academy of Science and Art was established in 1886, and the Slovenian Academy of Science and Art in 1938, the Academy of Science and Art of Bosnia and Herzegovina in 1966, the Macedonian Academy of Science and Art in 1967, the Academy of Science and Art of Kosovo in 1975 and the Academy of Science and Art of Vojvodina in 1979.

There is no unique pattern of membership. There are generally two types of members: regular members, who are life members, and corresponding members from whom the regular members are selected. In addition, some academies have associate members.

Each academy is organised in divisions, by scientific discipline or field of art. The Academies play an important role in the broad programming of research work, and they review the medium and long-term plans of each federal unit. The Academies are also active in evaluation of research results.

The academies are very active in international co-operation. The Council of Academies co-operates with about 15 foreign academies. In addition, each one of the academies of federal units co-operates directly with a large number of foreign academies. Numerous inter-academy meetings, and joint international scientific congresses are organised.

The financial resources of academies are determined by law. Besides these funds, academies get funds for their research programmes, as well as for their other functions (international and inter-academy co-operation, publishing, exhibitions, etc.) through the SCI for Science.

V. THE CLIMATE FOR INNOVATION

1. The macroeconomic climate

The economic and political climate in Yugoslavia in the 1970s and the first half of the 1980s have been characterised by:

- neglect of the selective role of the market;
- high distortions of costs, exchange rates and prices;
- the dominant influence of the administration on economic conditions, particularly on the allocation of domestic investment and foreign capital, as well as on quantitative limitations which reduced business autonomy, responsibility and the competitiveness of enterprises and banks.

To date, the economic policy measures applied have enabled numerous enterprises to reduce artificially their production costs, through:

- exemption from reimbursment of domestic and foreign debts;
- payment of high negative real interest rates for credits;
- acceptance without firm obligations to repay of undervalued social investments, convertible currency, etc.; and
- increasing added value by introducing quantitative import limitations, administrative or monopoly prices, etc.

In such conditions, the major part of the economy depends on administrative measures, without being compelled (except for exporters to highly demanding markets) or motivated to invest in personnel, technological, innovations, better organisation and management.

The 1983 Long Term Programme of Economic Stabilisation assigned a significant role to economic criteria to solve Yugoslavia's economic crisis. The basic target of the Programme was to increase the selective role of domestic and foreign markets, by gradual adjustment of personal income in relation to real productivity and by real pricing of energy, domestic and foreign capital (i.e. using real exchange rates and eliminating real negative interest rates).

Taking these parameters into account made it possible to detect those products and firms which, because of previous irrational investments and low quality of products, services, organisation and management were not able to pay the real costs of production and other outlays.

In the second half of 1985 and in 1986 the Federal Government did not succeed in resisting regional-political and monopolistic industrial pressures. As a consequence, non-rational cost and income redistribution increased after the second half of 1985.

In the present circumstances, it is difficult to determine the real earnings of individual enterprises. It is not clear, for example, whether for one dollar earned by export or import substitution the exchange rate should be 400, 1 000, 2 000, 3 000 dinnars or even more. The overvalued dinar (particularly in respect to hard currencies), negative real interest rates and the administrative allocation of hard currencies, foreign credits and domestic investment capital, serve to protect import-substituting industries rather than encourage the export-oriented sector. Domestic savings have declined, with unfavourable consequences for capital accumulation. Enterprises and banks have become even more dependent on government decisions and this has further worsened the macro-economic climate for innovation.

Yugoslavia's political leadership is in favour of the revitalisation of the economy through the more intensive application of economic efficiency criteria. One of the first steps in this direction is the improvement of the macro-economic climate for innovation. Economic "rehabilitation" requires a fundamental adaptation of the economic system through the selective role of the market and deep transformation of the planning mechanism, leading to introduction of qualitative development planning instead of quantitative planning.

The strengthening of market forces through adoption of criteria of economic efficiency is expected through the following steps:

- In spite of the expected structural, social and regional difficulties, the Yugoslav economy must reduce the existing disparities in line with the 1983 guidelines, by adjusting real personal income to productivity and by adjusting costs of domestic and foreign capital and energy to the real cost of these factors of production.
- On this basis, it is necessary to identify those enterprises with an operating deficit and, subsequently, take decisions to abandon part of productive capacity (by writing off investments) and undertake personnel, conceptual-strategic, technology and marketing programmes and financial rehabilitation of the remaining capacity. In addition, it is necessary to significantly improve investment criteria in the Yugoslav economy, by adopting internationally-recognised criteria.
- In accordance with the stabilisation-oriented current economic policy, Yugoslav economic policy should radically and consistently reduce existing inflationary trends in outlays and incomes as soon as possible and encourage domestic savings. This process would create more equal economic conditions in the country and lower the dependency of the economy on government, which in turn would stimulate the competitiveness and independence of banks and enterprises and thus improve the climate for innovation.

Through the planning of qualitative development, investment should be motivated to support the development of knowledge and innovations. Here, the most important points are the following:

- Cost reduction, improvement of the cost, quality and technological content of Yugoslav export goods and services, particularly those targeted at hard currency markets. In turn, this would make it possible for Yugoslavia to import efficient equipment and sophisticated intermediate goods.
- Stimulation of technological revitalisation of the Yugoslav economy, by selective introduction and effective application of technologies, support (by taxation policy, specific-purpose funds, etc.) of personnel policy and of research and development, etc.
- Enhancement of work efficiency, coupled with a reduction of unemployment, particularly in the less-developed regions of the country. This implies:
  - Reshaping large enterprises to orient them towards advanced technologies, involving the transfer of a number of peripheral production programmes to small

subcontractors. Growth of employment is linked to an increase of employment in a number of small subcontracting firms.

- Further development of the broad potential of small-scale enterprises (beside the above-mentioned subcontracting firms) ranging from conventional goods and services (particularly tourism) to scientific production and services. This process can also involve Yugoslav workers temporarily employed abroad.
- Reduction of unemployment in the less-developed regions of the country which is of particular importance for development of the country. The less-developed regions have a constant need for all kinds of knowledge relating to markets, production and personnel problems, etc. For these regions, intensive stimulation (including by financial means) of the creation of new workplaces, together with the provision of the necessary knowledge to improve the economic efficiency is a more appropriate approach than the former provision of cheap capital, without responsibility for the effectiveness of investment.

The adaptation of the existing socio-economic system is essential for any significant improvement of the macro-economic climate for innovation. Without a fundamental adaptation of the economic system, even the considerably higher investments in R&D planned and the technological strategy of the country will be ineffective.

2. The general state of innovation

The relatively recent opening of Yugoslavia to world technological trends, together with the underdevelopment inherited from the pre-war period, has led recently to an acute awareness of the importance of technological innovation and national creative endeavour for the country's development. Efforts to develop a comprehensive policy in the area of technological innovation – an area little explored in the context of the specific social system of Yugoslavia – have not so far resulted in substantial economic effects. As shown by the downward trend of the recently introduced and abandoned products in the Yugoslav industry (Figure 5) as well as the declining trend of the number of enterprises with newly introduced and abandoned products (Figure 6), the innovativeness of industrial organisations of associated labour is decreasing.

The basic legal framework of the country (the Yugoslav Constitution, the Republics' Constitutions, the Associated Labour Act and other regulations) recognises the importance of science and education as essential development factors, as well as rights and obligations of workers who are expected to improve and further develop the means of production which have been entrusted to them.

The agreement on stimulation of innovative activities at the national level, enacted in the mid-1970s, together with an agreement in the early 1980s on the foundations for technological development strategy in Yugoslavia lay down guidelines for the stimulation of innovative activities.

In spite of improvements in the status and place of innovators in research activities, the climate for innovation in Yugoslav society is still unfavourable. This can be explained by the general economic conditions as well as by a lack of motivation.

A number of factors have hampered industrial innovation: the increased risks associated with innovation as a consequence of the rapid change in economic conditions, the liberal import (at least until recently) of foreign technologies, price controls, socialisation of losses,

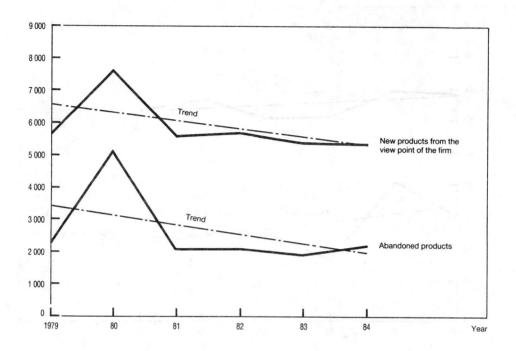

Figure 5. **NEW AND ABANDONED PRODUCTS IN YUGOSLAV INDUSTRY**

Source: The Yugoslav Federal Statistics Bureau; *Changes in Industrial Production Programme.*

inadequate technological infrastructure and assistance, and failure to take responsibility for financial risks.

If expenditures on mastering new production techniques are taken as an indicator of innovative activities, the example of Croatia shows that less than 8 per cent of all enterprises reported innovative activities in the period 1981-83, and that the share of these expenditures in total operating costs was very low.

Innovative projects undertaken by enterprises are financed mainly through their own funds, with limited resources from other organisations. Because of unstable economic conditions, enterprises are generally oriented towards short-term innovative projects. In the absence of the necessary capacity to utilise complex technologies there is no motivation to protect industrial property and to acquire domestically available technological solutions.

In spite of these unfavourable conditions, innovative processes are successful in some sectors – mainly in enterprises involved in international markets – and the results are encouraging.

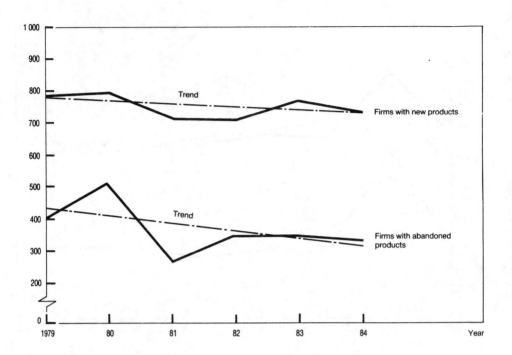

Figure 6. **FIRMS WITH NEW AND ABANDONED PRODUCTS**

Source: The Yugoslav Federal Statistics Bureau, *Changes in Industrial Production Programme.*

3.   Special support measures for innovative activities

During the last 10 years, systematic support of innovative activities has been limited to the more developed republics and regions. More recently, the banking system has initiated analyses of the most efficient ways of financing and evaluations of innovations. Some examples of this support are described below.

Since 1973, the "Ljubljanska Banka" has been dealing systematically with the problem of co-financing innovations. This organisation has enabled some 30 to 55 innovations to be made annually. It assists the innovation process by providing additional funds during the phases of development, testing and trial production, including the making and testing of prototypes. During this phase personnel are trained, and equipment and technical documentation prepared. Supplementary funds are provided for equipment, adaptation of installations, construction of pilot facilities and for market studies. Technological procedures for high quality and regular mass production are verified in a trial production phase.

The criteria for co-financing innovations are rigorous. An innovation should result in a new product, new technology or organisational improvement. It should be technologically, economically and financially sound. Preference is given to the further development of basic or applied research results, financed by the Self-Management Community of Interest of the Republic of Slovenia, by particular research communities or by organisations of associated labour. Priority is given to those projects covering the whole of the innovative chain where the responsibilities are borne by the same R&D team or group of experts.

In addition, the innovation should be compatible with principles of economic restructuring laid down by the long-term and medium-term plans of Yugoslavia and Slovenia. It should be a product or technology which is aimed at: production with good prospects on the world market; a rational substitution of imports; reducing energy consumption; decreasing the dependency on scarce or imported raw materials; stimulating technological progress; or improving the human environment.

The experience of the Ljubljanska Banka in the area of co-financing innovations during the last 13 years is very positive. During the last two years, the real value of funds was reduced because of a limited availability of long-term investment capital. On the average, 24.5 projects have been financed annually by loans amounting to 12.6 million dinars.

Up to the end of 1981, the SCI for Science of the Republic of Slovenia made available considerable funds for this purpose within the framework of an "agreement on joint provision of loan funds". The law on research activities, enacted in 1981, no longer permits such financial arrangements.

Additional difficulties arise from the total absence of risk capital. In the preparation and introduction of innovative projects, entreprises face considerable difficulty regarding finance for the final phases of the project. The experience of Ljubljanska Banka shows that only a relatively small number of firms are eligible for co-financing of innovations.

In 1982 the banks of Serbia, and the business associations of the banks of other republics and provinces operating in Serbia, the Republican Community for Science and the Chamber of Commerce of Republic of Serbia concluded an agreement defining uniform conditions and criteria for loans granted for R&D. According to this agreement:

- Loans for investment programmes in the area of industrial production with an estimated value of more than 500 million dinars would generally require that such programmes also include programmes for research and innovation related to production.
- If the estimated value exceeds 1 000 million dinars, loans would be granted on the condition that the investment programme also incorporates an R&D programme related to production.

Priority in granting loans is to be given to investments based on domestic technology and in particular on domestic R&D results. In the framework of this agreement, banks have agreed to grant loans for R&D activities aimed at mastering new production techniques or technologies, improving existing production or technologies, introducing up-to-date technical solutions, upgrading organisational work, foreign market research and performing production trials.

The amount of funds made available for R&D loans is to be determined by the banks' annual plans. Loan conditions are the following:

- The programme is in accordance with the established development priorities;
- The programme is in accordance with development plans of the production organisation for the relevant economic sector;
- The aim of the investment is the continuation of applied research carried out by a domestic scientific research organisation or a firm;

- The investment is verified by the Serbian Republic's SCI for Science and the Chamber of Commerce; and
- The loan seeker is creditworthy and must submit a detailed business plan.

Loans are to be granted at a "privileged" interest rate determined each year by the bank's authorised body with the repayment period not exceeding five years. The "privileged" interest rate is 50 per cent of the regular rate. The first repayments are due 6-12 months later, which means that they cannot be made from income earned by the new technology. Consequently, risk is to be borne by the credit user. The Agreement came into force at the beginning of 1984, but it is still not applied in practice; no project had been financed at the time that this report was prepared.

In Croatia, it is proposed to establish a Bank for Innovation granting loans under more favourable conditions than usual. In 1969, the Chamber of Commerce of Zagreb started a fund to help its members improve existing products and develop new ones. Interest-free loans, with a repayment term of 4 years, are granted on the basis of an open competition procedure conducted once year. Criteria for selection of projects include: export orientation, import substitution, the use of domestic raw materials and semi-manufactured goods, energy efficiency, employment, marketing, influence on small industry development, efficiency of expended funds, stimulation of domestic creativity and development of the loan seeking organisation. It was envisaged that the funds should come from voluntarily pooled resources of the organisations of associated labour, from donations and funds of the socio-political communities and other bodies dealing with R&D, as well as from the Chamber's surplus income and savings.

Until now, the only funds available have come from the Chamber's savings, thus considerably limiting the possibility of co-financing (about 2 million dinars per project in 1986). As a rule, these funds have been used to co-finance up to 25 per cent of the cost of projects of small enterprises. Up to 1987, loans have been granted to 41 organisations. This aid seems to have been used efficiently. Innovations achieved have significantly stimulated growth and employment, mainly in small organisations. However, apart from the savings of the Chamber, no other resources have been made available in spite of the interest manifested by an increasing number of firms. Since the outlays of the Chamber are growing rapidly, prospects for increase in this support are not good.

In Croatia, joint financing of programmes of "priority research and regional interest projects", partially from funds of the SCI for Science and partially from enterprises constitute an instrument for the stimulation of innovation. This approach links science to economic development and to the particular development orientations of the region.

All Republics and Provinces concluded an agreement in 1975 to adopt taxation policies in all federal units favouring R&D. This includes tax relief to inventors and authors of technological improvements, and favourable tax treatment for funds invested in R&D, inventive and innovative activities.

Because the enactment of the taxation law is entrusted to Republics and Provinces, the agreement has been applied differently throughout the country. For example, in Slovenia since 1974, all income received by authors of inventions, technological improvements, useful proposals and other innovations is exempted from income tax. In Vojvodina, tax concessions are envisaged for investors. Since the adoption of the Programme of Economic Stabilisation in 1983, there has been a more systematic approach to the promotion of innovation. At the federal level, the new agreement on the co-ordination of the taxation system should be used to stimulate innovation. Relevant amendments to federal and republic legislation have been drafted.

Current approaches to promoting innovation fall in three categories: firstly, measures to encourage enterprises to earmark funds for R&D and innovative work; secondly taxation policy measures; and thirdly systems-related policy measures, described above.

In relation to the first category, until recently the funds earmarked for R&D by enterprises and other organisations, even if directly linked to development, were not considered as operating expenditure, but were treated as expenditure from income. A first step was to recognise the research work as material expenditure for their current needs. By the enactment of the federal law on global income and revenue in 1986, this form of stimulation of investment in R&D was extended so as to treat all R&D outlays as operating expenditure, even in cases when services of other scientific research and research development organisations are used. These funds are not subject to any tax or contribution payment.

The 1986 Federal Law on depreciation of capital investments stipulates that innovation funds and funds for acquisition of material rights to technology are subject to depreciation. Innovation funds include investments in all forms of innovation, as well as rationalisation and other long-term improvements of work and production conditions. Material rights to technology include patent, industrial sample models and trade marks. Calculation of depreciation is based on expenses for the preparation of studies, projects and technical and technological documentation with a view to introducing new or improved technological procedures, as well as for expenses related to preparation of such procedures. The annual depreciation rate for funds used for innovations and acquisition of material rights ranges from 20 to 30 per cent.

As regards the second category (i.e. taxation policy measures), the legislation comes within the competence of the different federal units, while the co-ordination is performed through the agreement at the federal level. The manner in which taxation policy exerts an influence on the innovative behaviour in Serbia will be used as an illustrative example of a federal unit and the Commune Pula in Croatia as an illustration of a smaller region.

In Serbia the first attempts to encourage research activities were made in 1983, with a law exempting scientific research organisations from republic income tax, on the condition that exempted funds be pooled with other organisations and used for strengthening research. This provision, which has been in force for 3 years, has given good results.

Organisations producing certain electronic and communications equipment are also exempted from the republic income tax, on condition that at least 10 per cent of their income is earmarked for strengthening the material base for labour and investment in the electronics development programmes planned by the agreement on the development of electronics in the period 1986-90.

Other proposals, not yet translated into law, include tax exemption for the share of income of which the production firms invests in research work, and relief of certain payments to employees of the share of income earned from the exploitation of domestic research and resulting technologies.

Stimulation of the innovative behaviour of individuals through taxation policy measures in Serbia is, at present, rather limited. Personal income from patent and technical improvements is subject to income tax, after deduction of costs incurred. These costs include expenses incurred in obtaining patent protection and outlays for production of the first prototype. A tax reduction of 50 per cent is available only when the taxpayer transfers his patent to an organisation of associated labour.

The Commune Pula provides a particularly interesting example of a community which exempts from communal sales tax, in the first two years, production and sales of products, manufactured and marketed in the territory of the commune. According to local businessmen, this measure has given good results, and stimulated local innovative activity. Furthermore, in

Croatia, income from patents and technical improvements handed over to firms is exempted from the republic tax on personal income.

The exemption from custom duties and other import taxes of equipment used exclusively in R&D is another incentive for R&D and innovation. This measure is available to registered research organisations.

There are no adequate service mechanisms in the area of industrial property. About ten organisations located in most republics and provinces serve as documentation sources in the area of protection of industrial property and ensure follow-up action at the Federal Patent Office (Patentivnest, Sarajevo; Office for registration of patents, Ljubljana; Centre for work productivity improvement and SIATUH, Croatia; etc.).

Some organisations have an appropriate data base with lists of patents and links to technological data bases abroad (Inpadoc, Derwent, Predicast, etc.). They are able to provide high quality information and to investigate technology trends in particular sectors.

The low level of patent activity and of utilisation of patent and other information for technological and market research is mainly due to inefficient organisation and insufficient capacity on the part of the enterprises with respect to development, transfer and marketing of innovations. There is also a lack of patent specialists.

Scientific and technical libraries are established mainly in university institutions (reference centres, national and university libraries, and faculties). Specialised organisations which also collect literature in certain fields and provide appropriate reviews, abstracts, or reference data include the Yugoslav centre for scientific and technical documentation and information in Belgrade and the Yugoslav bibliographic institute (CDI) in Zagreb. The development and better utilisation of the scientific and technical literature is limited by the capacity to continuously update information.

There are practically no specialised agencies or organisations for technical assistance in the fields of development and application of innovations. The law on protection of inventions, technical improvements and trademarks obliges the enterprises to assist their employees to undertake and protect their innovations. However, most enterprises lack the capacity to provide such services. According to a survey carried out in Croatia, nearly all innovations, new products, inventions, technical improvements and useful proposals have taken place in enterprises with between 126 and 1 000 employees.

An innovation centre with appropriate data bases of domestic and foreign technologies, which can also supply related contracting services, has recently started in Slovenia. This small agency (NOVUM) for marketing domestic R&D results is operating with about 600 innovators (mainly individuals) from Slovenia and Croatia.

The Institute for Marketing, Business and Management at Ljubljana has developed, in co-operation with the Chamber of Commerce of Slovenia, a special data base of technologies available for transfer. Enterprises and individuals can obtain information free of charge from a data base which uses international patent and goods classifications. Business and copyright secrecy is guaranteed, since only general information is supplied. The data base comprises 5 280 foreign and 658 domestic innovations. Initiatives for creation of a similar data base for technological innovations are underway in Belgrade and Zagreb.

4. Motivation and training of workers for innovation

Special forms of remuneration aiming at stimulating the innovative behaviour of employees include payments and rewards, career advancement, priority in housing grants, as well as loans and tax concessions.

Along with other factors influencing the innovative climate within enterprises, a poorly developed system of material rewards has been the main reason for insufficient motivation of workers to innovate. It is estimated that there are less than 5 per cent of the total employed population are active innovators. Individual income from innovations is very low, especially as this type of reward is often shared by several persons.

Although not limited to innovators, many enterprises provide tuition-free additional education (particularly permanent education) as means of motivation. Career advancement of innovators towards managerial positions most often leads to the abandonment of creative activities.

The motivation instrument which is the most used is public recognition. Individual innovators receive prizes, diplomas, charters, medals, etc. However, this kind of reward has not been sufficiently developed at the level of enterprises. During the last few years the tendency has been to motivate innovators by awards of visits to technology fairs and exhibitions of innovations; and more particularly by public presentation of their inventions in the country and abroad, as well as by participation in different symposia devoted to technological creativity.

The activities of individual inventors gets relatively little coverage in the daily press, radio and TV, by comparison with the other types of information (sport, culture, etc.) provided by these media.

5. Public promotion of innovation

It is generally considered that public promotion of innovative behaviour constitutes an important component of national innovation policy measures. These measures include campaigns made by numerous socio-political and professional organisations, and articles in the news media. These media can facilitate the exchange of information between innovators and to support their interests. However, insufficient funding and the shortage of skilled personnel limit this type of dissemination of technical culture and popularisation of science and technology.

Among the first initiatives for disseminating the technical culture (under the slogan "science for the people"), the organisation "Popular Technology" started as a group of modelling enthusiasts. Its activities are now centred around many professional associations: radio-amateurs, the Aeronautical Association, the Association of Inventors, photo and cinema clubs, "Science for Youth", the "Nicola Tesla" movement and the touring clubs. Numerous experts have been trained thanks to these hobby activities. Initiatives like "Science for the Youth" and the "Nikola Tesla movement" seem to have been successful in educating and orienting young people in research methodology.

In a similar vein, there is also the Association of Inventors and Authors of Technical Improvements of Yugoslavia, with republic and provincial associations. Apart from the training of inventors, the protection of their interests and the provision of legal advice, the Association carries out campaigns for recognition of innovation and better remuneration of inventive work. It also contributes to the organisation of exhibitions at regional and international level ("RAST YU", "INOVA", etc.), and promotes "the Home of Innovators".

The Yugoslav Association of Engineers and Technicians, in addition to its professional-educational functions, deals with problems of the creation and implementation of technological development strategies in the country.

The Federation of Labour Unions and other socio-political organisations have taken action during the last few years to stimulate the technological creativity of employees. To this end specialised bodies or sections have been created.

6. Technological co-operation with foreign countries

Technological and economic co-operation between Yugoslav firms and foreign companies has been characterised by contractual agreements including licensing contracts, long-term production co-operation, commercial-technical co-operation, joint ventures, etc. Technological co-operation with foreign countries has been regulated since 1979 by the law on technology transfer which requires federal approval. This takes place through a complex procedure in which the economic utility of individual contracts is examined.

Acquisition of material rights to technology (licences) and long-term production co-operation has been practised most frequently. The number of licence contracts for purchase of technology is decreasing, as well as the number of commercial-technical co-operation contracts. There is a slight increase of joint venture contracts and a considerable increase of long-term production contracts. These are at present the dominant form of economic and technological co-operation between Yugoslavia and foreign countries.

A number of licences have been purchased for technologies which are in current use but are not state-of-the-art. These have often included restrictive clauses imposed by foreign partners. Such clauses have limited utilisation of the acquired technologies, limited exports, restricted further development of the acquired technological know-how, restricted raw material and semi-manufacture supply from other suppliers, etc. Yugoslavia's bargaining power has been very weak because of the lack of qualified personnel, organisational deficiencies, frequent changes in regulations and the absence of a long-term technological strategy at the national level. According to various professional sources, the relatively liberal treatment of technology imports has not contributed to the advancement of domestic R&D potential and innovation.

Some 126 licence agreements on the purchase of technology in operation in 1983 generated a total production in that year of 19.5 billion dinars, while the licence payments amounted to 450 million dinars – less than 3 per cent of production. Although 40 per cent of this production was exported, these exports contained less than 20 per cent of imported components. At the end of the 1970s, Yugoslav payments for licences amounted to about 0.5 per cent of total exports. The corresponding figure for other countries were: 2.5 per cent for Argentina, 5.1 per cent for Brazil, 4.4 per cent for India and 0.6 per cent for South Korea.

The quality of licence agreements improved in the 1980s as a consequence of the enactment of the law on technology transfer, implementation of the procedure of contract acceptability, and the Agreement on the technological development strategy of Yugoslavia (established at federal level) which sets out some criteria for technologies appropriate for Yugoslavia.

Long-term production co-operation with foreign partners plays an important role in Yugoslav industry – including technological co-operation, joint programming of production, specialisation, trade, etc. In the period 1968-86, these contracts were concluded most frequently in electric machinery and equipment production (15 per cent), transportation facilities production (12 per cent), machine-building industry (10 per cent) and electrical home appliances production (9 per cent).

Through a mutual exchange of products and product components, these contracts have helped to upgrade the production programmes of domestic manufacturers. This form of co-operation developed more rapidly than other contractual forms, because the acquisition of technology was possible in the framework of long-term production co-operation and payments could be made through counter-supply of goods, or for imports of general consumption goods of the same value (a 100 per cent right to foreign currencies earned by exports).

Joint ventures are considered to provide a relatively rapid and secure flow of technological know-how. On the Yugoslav side, the basic motive for setting up such entreprises was acquisition of technology and capital access to international markets. In the last two years, about 70 contracts have been concluded, but these include a number of small projects which are hardly likely to influence the production structure or to change it through technological revitalisation.

Changes in 1984 did not lead to a notable increase in foreign capital investment, which is about 20 per cent of total investment in joint ventures. The main reasons for this is instability of the Yugoslav economy, the high inflation rate, protection of the domestic industry against international competition, and complex foreign trade and foreign exchange legislation which does not offer to foreign investors enough guarantees for reducing business risks. An amendment to the 1985 law on joint ventures has reduced many previous limitations and risks for foreign partners and this should result in a more rapid development of this form of economic-technological co-operation.

7. Indicators of scientific, technological and innovative performance

Official statistics include three categories of indicators:

- Published studies by scientific discipline, classified in three groups (in-house, national and foreign publications);
- Completed work by type of research (fundamental, applied, and development); and
- Numbers of the reported and registered patents of the scientific research organisations.

The SCI for Science provide some data on results applied in production and numbers of new MSc and PhD degrees acquired through involvement in particular R&D projects. These data are not very reliable.

a) Indicators of scientific output

The average productivity, measured by the number of published studies per researcher is virtually the same in institutes and university faculties. This demonstrates an equal interest for publishing research results. By scientific disciplines, there are great differences, especially with regard to studies published in foreign reviews. In the natural and physical sciences, researchers in institutes publish almost 70 per cent more than researchers in university faculties, and twice as much abroad as researchers in university faculties. In comparison with other disciplines, researchers in natural sciences publish much more in foreign reviews.

Because of their prevalent involvement in R&D tasks conducted for enterprises (the results of which are not usually published), researchers in the technical and technological sciences in institutes used to publish less than the staff of technical faculties. However during

63

the last two years the institutes published almost as much as the teaching staff, although three times less than in foreign reviews.

In the field of biotechnical sciences, faculty researchers publish twice as frequently as researchers in institutes. The latter group reports the lowest number of studies in foreign publications in comparison with other scientific fields. Although by this measure the overall productivity of the biotechnical sciences is higher than in technical sciences, publishing abroad is lower. Overall productivity and foreign publishing in the medical sciences is high and ranks immediately after the natural sciences. In the field of social sciences and humanities, faculty researchers publish much less in comparison with researchers in institutes.

In Yugoslavia, publishing of research results can be generally evaluated as follows:

- Scientific workers manifest a great interest for publishing their studies ("publish or perish");
- Publishing in foreign reviews is maintained at a relatively high level in the fields of natural and medical sciences and is increasing in technical sciences and humanities; and
- In social sciences, productivity and publishing abroad is the lowest (3 per cent in relation to the average of 15 per cent).

The number of "completed scientific studies" can indicate some characteristics and tendencies, but it is not entirely reliable. In spite of this, this indicator permits basic comparisons within the Yugoslav scientific research system. It can best be used to compare the number of published studies with the number of completed studies per researcher per year in research organisations and university faculties.

As far as the institutes are concerned, the number of completed studies per researcher is constantly and considerably higher than the indicator of published studies. Such "high" productivity is apparently the result of an extreme "chopping up" of articles.

The number of studies published by faculty teaching staff is almost equal to the number of studies per researcher in the institutes. The number of completed research studies per university professor is three times lower than studies per researcher in the institutes, which reflects the time spent on research projects for external customers.

b) Technological and innovation indicators

Several indicators in the area of technology and innovation have already been cited (new and abandoned products, technical improvements, useful proposals, indicators of the volume of innovative activities in the economy, etc.). Here only two indicators of research activity and innovation are considered: patents, and balance of imports and exports by technological intensity of product.

Yugoslavia has been a signatory of the Paris Convention on Protection of Industrial Property since 1921 when the Office for Protection of Industrial Property was founded . The Patent Office was established after World War II, and recently reorganised as the Federal Patent Office – the national agency for protection of industrial property in Yugoslavia.

Patent data in Tables 23 and 24 show the following:

- The number of applications for patents, both in absolute and relative terms, is low in comparison with other OECD countries;
- Domestic applications show a slight increase up to 1983 (index 1983-82 = 102) and from then on, they decline (index 1984-83 = 94);

Table 22. Completed and published scientific research studies per researcher – 1978-84

	1978	1979	1980	1981	1982	1983	1984
Research organisations							
Completed	0.77	0.92	0.95	0.94	0.91	0.91	0.88
Published	0.69	0.70	0.62	0.58	0.64	0.66	0.60
Faculties							
Completed (all researchers)	0.19	0.24	0.34	0.27	0.29	0.27	0.28
Completed (per FTE researcher)	0.47	0.61	0.84	0.68	0.73	0.68	0.70
Published (all researchers)	0.46	0.70	0.76	0.62	0.60	0.66	0.70

Source: See Table 1.

Table 23. **Applied for, *Ad acta* and registered patents**

Year	Applied for	*Ad acta*	Registered
1970	1 297	2	1
1971	2 250	2	8
1972	2 690	7	4
1973	3 050	4	8
1974	3 206	9	5
1975	3 295	47	135
1976	3 309	236	204
1977	2 951	1 521	199
1978	3 032	2 202	331
1979	3 346	2 219	555
1980	3 225	2 551	720
1981	2 945	2 774	709
1982	2 943	2 648	419
1983	2 481	4 225	141
1984	2 212	3 783	18
1985	1 309	1 766	16

Source: Data base, Science and Technology Policy Research Center, Institute Mihajlo Pupin, Belgrade.

Table 24. **Applied for, *Ad acta* and registered patents by republic, province, and foreign reporters – 1970-85**

Territory	Applied for	*Ad acta*	Registered
Serbia	6 145	3 634	121
Vojvodina	1 384	823	19
Kosovo	176	126	3
Croatia	3 904	1 914	165
Slovenija	2 714	1 236	180
Bosnia-Herzegovina	1 252	739	22
Montenegro	222	102	4
Macedonia	733	426	12
Total Yugoslavia	16 530	9 000	526
Foreign patents	27 011	14 996	2 947

Source: Ibid.

- There is a decline in applications by foreign inventors during the years 1975-77 and also from 1979 to 1985 (index 1984-79 = 40, index 1984-83 = 82);
- The percentage of registered patents in relation to *ad acta* applications is extremely low. From 1970 to 1985, 3.19 per cent of patent applications were registered and 54.4 per cent of applications were put *ad acta*;
- The registration procedure takes a very long time: on average more than six years. In 1970 the Federal Patent Office passed from a national to international patent classification system and reorganised its administration; and
- Applications by individuals are by far the most numerous and those by institutes very rare, in spite of their high quality. Enterprises account for the largest share of registered patents, but the number of their applications is extremely low.

In the period 1970-85 the largest number of patent applications has been in the following sections of the international patent classification: B – processing and treatment, traffic and transportation, F – mechanical engineering, lighting/heating, armaments and mining.

Since 1979 the balance of trade statistics includes two categories of products: technology-intensive (Table 25) and technology non-intensive (Table 26). In recent years,

Table 25   **International trade in technology-intensive products**
Exports and imports in current million dinars

Group of products		1979	1980	1981	1982	1983	1984
Computers and other equipment	export	342	489	503	966	1 295	2 898
for data processing	import	3 697	4 930	3 522	8 127	6 066	1 217
	e/i	0.0926	0.0992	0.1428	0.1189	0.2135	0.2307
Equipment for electric power	export	1 761	3 384	4 159	9 284	10 340	19 740
transfer and distributions	import	4 118	5 426	5 688	9 993	8 547	16 659
	e/i	0.4275	0.6238	0.7313	0.9291	1.2099	1.1849
Professional and scientific	export	996	1 986	2 710	6 011	3 667	8 681
instruments	import	5 321	6 057	6 612	10 345	10 673	20 498
	e/i	0.1873	0.3279	0.4099	0.5811	0.8436	0.4235
Medecines	export	2 288	4 664	6 901	13 835	10 646	19 673
	import	1 844	2 706	3 289	4 295	5 664	10 206
	e/i	1.2411	1. 7233	2.0983	3.2215	1.8796	1.9276
Synthetic and plastic	export	2 363	4 124	5 764	10 306	9 590	20 248
materials	import	9 189	14 198	14 594	28 133	19 211	58 246
	e/i	0.2572	0.2905	0.3949	0.3663	0.3283	0.3475
Turbines and generators	export	1 124	2 393	2 425	5 624	5 359	11 357
	import	4 117	5 539	6 029	9 013	10 129	18 008
	e/i	0.2730	0.4321	0.4023	0.6240	0.5291	0.6307
Agricultural chemicals	export	1 922	4 710	3 964	5 826	6 128	10 908
	import	1 182	2 469	3 297	6 460	6 379	13 712
	e/i	1.6261	1.8420	1.2360	0.9022	0.9606	0.7956
Industrial chemicals	export	1 143	1 995	2 751	6 070	7 030	19 669
	import	12 007	18 179	19 696	34 140	39 591	81 394
	e/i	0.0952	0.1598	0.1397	0.1680	0.1776	0.2417
Radio and TV sets	export	403	750	805	1 961	1 952	3 965
	import	1 650	2 022	1 537	2 597	2 956	5 753
	e/i	0.2447	0.3708	0.5241	0.7551	0.6604	0.6891
Metal treatment machines	export	1 922	3 106	4 225	11 484	11 966	2 143
and equipment	import	8 706	9 761	10 549	36 045	19 812	36 079
	e/i	0.2336	0.3183	0.4005	0.4409	0.6040	0.5943

Source: Data base, Science and Technology Policy Research Center, The Mihajlo Pupin Institute, Belgrade.

Table 26 **International trade in non-technology-intensive products**
Exports and imports in current million dinars

Group of products		1979	1980	1981	1982	1983	1984
Agricultural machinery and equipment	export	1 264	2 549	3 428	6 210	4 335	9 366
	import	2 663	2 598	2 878	6 748	6 053	7 693
	e/i	0.4746	0.9810	1.1911	0.9203	0.7163	1.2175
Motor vehicles and equipment	export	5 549	11 099	14 172	26 337	26 140	52 142
	import	14 217	14 753	16 113	30 013	24 489	45 483
	e/i	0.3903	0.7523	0.8795	0.8775	1.06774	1.1464
Electrical equipment	export.	1 637	2 691	4 066	10 447	11 717	21 480
	import.	1 982	2 856	2 913	4 544	3 834	7 404
	e/i	0.8263	1.0227	1.3955	2.2991	2.0559	2.9011
Construction, mining and similar equipment	export	1 836	2 775	4 446	11 705	11 170	26 803
	import	9 587	12 295	9 003	14 066	11 753	25 285
	e/i	0.1915	0.2258	0.4938	0.8322	0.9504	1.0560
Other chemical products	export	1 747	3 539	5 912	11 474	11 053	23 220
	import	3 802	6 314	6 511	9 694	13 387	22 454
	e/i	0.4597	0.5605	0.9080	1.1836	0.8509	1.0344
Metal-working products	export	3 768	6 336	7 638	18 456	18 006	28 554
	import	4 298	5 272	6 034	9 260	8 997	12 960
	e/i	0.8766	1.2017	1.2659	1.9931	1.7790	2.2033
Rubber and plastics products	export	301	653	976	1 989	1 882	3 987
	import	1 400	1 874	1 804	2 892	2 718	5 568
	e/i	0.2154	0.3485	0.5416	0.6882	0.8938	0.7161
Glass, stone and clay products	export	335	652	789	1 452	2 277	2 617
	import	240	312	366	693	990	1 338
	e/i	1.3948	2.0887	2.1538	2.0922	2.0164	1.9582
Non-ferrous metals and products out of them	export	3 214	4 426	5 542	12 438	22 069	20 809
	import	296	498	791	1 474	1 927	8 505
	e/i	7.4565	8.8410	7.0008	8.4374	3.3428	3.4467

Source: Data base, Science and Technology Policy Research Center, The Mihajlo Pupin Institute, Belgrade.

foreign trade has been strongly influenced by the negative balance of payments. This led to exports "under all circumstances" and imports only if necessary. The trend of the export/import indicator over these years was the following:

– Exports exceed imports in the category of technology-intensive products with exception of pharmaceuticals, the production of which depends to a large extent on imported inputs, and which are exported mainly to less competitive markets. Electric power transfer and distribution equipment is in the same category.
– The ratio of non technology-intensive product exports/imports, with small exceptions, is generally over 1.0. This ratio is influenced by export/import and other policies.
– On the basis of their technological content, the competitiveness of the Yugoslav products is low, but this is compensated by considerably lower export prices.
– If this policy, in force during the years 1978-86, were to be continued, external debt repayments would have to be drawn exclusively from exports based on a low level of domestic development, further worsening the economic structure, and implying risks of further intensification of unemployment and diminution of the living standard.

For the sake of a long-term improvement of national competitiveness, export/import policy needs to be closely linked to technological development and intensive development of human and natural resources of the country. This applies even to sectors like tourism, which represent a great export and development opportunity provided that the technological component reaches a competitive level.

Indicators of international competitiveness and other information suggest that the Yugoslav economic structure is not sufficiently competitive. The technological level and almost non-existant innovative behaviour of the service sector leaves it incapable of contributing to improved competitiveness and to development of the economy. A favourable innovation climate and innovative behaviour together with an overall national awareness are indispensable both for production and service sectors.

VI. SCIENCE AND TECHNOLOGY PLANNING

1. Planning in Yugoslavia

The planning of research and development in Yugoslavia is carried out at different levels:

- Those producing scientific results (research institutes, faculties, enterprises, etc.), and those who use the results;
- The branch and sector associations;
- The federal units (republics and autonomous provinces); and
- The national level.

The planning process at these levels is extremely diverse. It covers all activities from fundamental to commercial research. There are differences in the planning procedure itself, in the contents of plans and in the periods of time necessary for their preparation. Thus, in practice, the planning of R&D is not undertaken in a national integrated system.

The concept of a national R&D planning system would be in accordance with the law setting up the principles of the planning system, which binds all those responsible. It would be based on the following two principles:

- Simultaneous planning by all involved groups which, within their rights and responsibilities prepare, enact and carry out plans. This principle requires strong planning discipline, and implies full responsibility of the part of all planners.
- Continuous planning which implies continuous adjustement and flexibility with regard to new conditions and circumstances during the period of realisation of the plan. In order to reconcile the various interests and planning targets during the formulation of the plan, those responsible for planning apply methods of self-management, mutual understanding and consultation.

Up to now, these two principles as well as self-management, understanding and consultation by those responsible for planning (especially consultations between the producers and users of R&D results), have not been entirely respected in practice. Nevertheless, the procedure leads to the formulation of plans which include, to a greater or lesser extent, all necessary basic elements: targets, tasks, most important planning activities for the realisation of these targets and tasks, necessary resources and ways of creating appropriate indicators of results.

2. Planning at the level of basic organisations of associated labour

In accordance with the law concerning the planning system in the area of associated labour, the basic organisation of associated labour (BOAL) is the main body responsible for planning. This may be changed in the near future. Planning practice has already deviated from this norm in most cases, especially in the area of R & D where is was hardly appropriate. At the level of basic organisations of associated labour and more often at the level of associations of BOAL, planning of R & D is carried out only:

- With those users of research results who have their own research units or centres;
- In cases where R & D activities represent an essential part of operations, particularly of large business projects involving major investment; and
- In the rarest case where enterprises regularly obtain R & D results through co-operation with some scientific research organisation.

In the absence of a strong and real interest for research results (except the interest shown through demand and purchase of technologies, licences etc. – usually abroad) the formal and political pressure on enterprises usually ends up in financing research in the framework of medium-term plans.

Enterprises which are expected to use the results of R & D usually meet the formal requirements by concluding some kind of contract with a scientific research organisation, and thus avoid possible criticism.

Those enterprises having their own R & D units or centres, plan the development and utilisation of R & D results on a medium-term or annual basis. In the case of decentralised enterprises, R & D is handled through commercial contracts even with their own internal research units. These units are more closely involved in meeting the production needs.

The underdevelopment of R & D planning within enterprises cannot be considered as a consequence of a shortcomings of methodologies but as a result of:

- Low motivation of the economy to invest in such kinds of activities;
- Prevailing short-term business attitude;
- Priority given to buying technology instead of creating it; and
- Inapplicability of research results in some cases where contracts are concluded with research organisations.

In spite of the short-term focus, the absence of economic criteria and sanctions for financial losses, and protection of mediocrity, the economy has tried to respond in the best possible way. Thus as soon as the need for a new technology was perceived, it was decided to buy it, thus minimising the risk of investment involved in development of new technology.

3. Planning at the sectoral level

The planning of scientific research activities at the branch or sectoral level (groups of products, groups of enterprises, etc.) is more developed, but there are large differences between sectors. In sectors with their "own" institutes which have established long-term co-operation with other specialised institutes (a good example is electric power industry), there is good short and medium-term planning of research activities. The chambers of commerce play an important role in planning scientific research activities, mainly at the level of federal units rather than at the national level.

Virtually no inter-sectoral planning of scientific research activities exists. The autonomy of each branch constitutes a barrier to effective planning of such scientific research activities.

4. Planning at the level of federal units

Planning of scientific research activities at the level of federal units is the most developed for obvious reasons: all the other categories of planning are also the most developed at this level; there are also republic and provincial communities for science which distribute funds and planning is an instrument of allocation of these funds.

While detailed procedures differ from one federal unit to another, the essence of planning is generally similar. It can be illustrated by the example of the Republic of Serbia. Medium-term and annual plans are formulated at the Republic level. These plans should, as far as possible, conform with the needs for scientific research work and the conditions for fulfilment of these needs.

The first stage starts one year, or eighteen months prior to the beginning of the five-year planning period, with the definition of national developmental needs, planning targets and tasks.

Planning experience suggests that there has not been sufficient capability to define clearly both the research needs and the expected role of scientific research at this level. The major role in defining these needs is played by research organisations, which naturally put more emphasis on their internal developmental aspirations than on real needs for science.

After determination of needs, planning targets and tasks, the definition of research programmes and projects begins. These are submitted by individual research organisations (independent institutes, faculties, research units within enterprises), with an analysis of compliance, appropriateness and quality of these proposals in relation to needs, planning targets and tasks.

During these phases planning is necessary at the level of scientific disciplines and fields. The funds allocated to research by the SCI for Science are usually broken down by scientific field. This allocation of funds is influenced strongly by tradition and also by the development policy for particular scientific fields. The necessity of taking account of traditional patterns seems to be justified in the case of research which is neither mission nor user oriented (other types of research are only co-financed).

The third phase consists in the allocation of available funds to specific proposals. As may be expected, requests always exceed available funds. This problem is solved:

- primarily by reducing funds requested for projects;
- to a lesser extent, by elimination of a considerable number of proposals; and
- in a limited number of cases, by fundamental changes in the mode of allocation of available funds to the republican SCI for Science.

In addition to the SCI for Science, the chambers of commerce, government agencies for science and technology and other interested bodies are involved in the planning process. This collective planning is extremely important in determining the relative and absolute amounts of funds available to the republic SCI for Science.

One of the main objectives of planning is to formulate large-scale projects in order to ensure research capacities with critical mass, to pool the activities of a large number of research organisations and to direct them to selected research tasks, while minimising duplication. This has been partly achieved, since the "zero sum game" principle has a strong influence on the behaviour of planners (see Chapter II).

Annual planning of research activities at the level of federal units is, as a rule, a simple disaggregation of medium-term plans. Most often, it is unnecessary and represents a superfluous bureaucratic procedure rather than a useful tool of planning.

In addition to scientific research, planning at the level of federal units also includes R & D investment, training of research personnel, acquisition of scientific literature and international research co-operation. The central problem here is the shortage of funds.

5. Planning at national level

There has been virtually no planning of scientific research policy at national level during the past two decades. This was a natural consequence of the shortage of funds allocated for these activities at national level and of the particular interpretation of the basic principles (see Chapter II). Scientific activities carried out at the national level of Federation (almost exclusively international scientific co-operation) were usually planned as a simple addition of individual plans of the federal units, since each of these was self-financing its share of activities at the national level. Scientific activities of common concern at the national level were planned on the same basis.

Within the Association of communities for scientific activities of Yugoslavia, the Committee for Scientific Policy and the Committee of Republic and Provincial projects adopts a medium-term plan. Up to now, this has been more a concept than a real plan. To a great extent, the medium-term plan of the Association reflects principles, aspirations and directions of science policy rather than constituting an operational plan. Joint projects have served mainly as a means for maintaining a minimum belief in the necessity of planning and implementation of science policy at the national level, rather than as a scientific approach to common problems. In reality, planning of science policy at the national level has amounted to an addition of individual policies of federal units without any internal consistency.

Science policy planning at national level is now begining to change. The first change was the abandonment of the principle by which each federal unit had to self-finance its share of joint projects of the Association. This has resulted in the adoption of joint projects without a disaggregation by republic and provincial sub-project (see Chapter VII). Another change was under way in the first half of 1987, with the adoption of the Strategy of Technological Development of Yugoslavia and creation of the Fund for Promotion of Technological Development at the national level (see Chapters III and IV).

6. Policy co-ordination

The co-ordination and implementation of science policy plans encounters enormous difficulties, even where planning is relatively well organised (e.g. at the level of the federal units) since the principles of decentralisation and democracy are implemented mainly in the general planning procedure but not necessarily in complex and concrete planning. Decentralisation brings with it multiplication of organisations, similar projects, research facilities and equipment. This can be partly explained by the fact that the information system is underdeveloped, so that individual organisations are not familiar with the activities and equipment of other organisations. Co-ordination of science policy planning is poor even in the area of large enterprises, because of the self-sufficient attitude of each unit.

Co-ordination of research projects in which several organisations, or research groups, participate is difficult, even when the participation of researchers from one or more scientific organisations is necessary.

Co-ordination is aimed at improving the formulation and implementation of plans, and to enable more effective utilisation of resources and capacities. Improved co-ordination is the first target of the future science, research, technology and development policies. This improvement can be accomplished only by defining clear responsibilities and by providing appropriate sanctions in the case of inadequate results. The basic limitation lies in the system of values on the basis of which the relationships needed for joint activities are formulated. From the methodological point of view, planning of science policy in Yugoslavia can be performed in the most up-to-date way, provided that there exists an appropriate socio-political, cultural and economic climate, as well as the necessary agreement for planned and co-ordinated science and technology development. Co-ordination does not effect the autonomy and independence of individual partners and planners. On the contrary, it makes their planning effective.

VII. TOWARDS SCIENCE-BASED DEVELOPMENT

1. The political climate

In the course of last few years, under the influence of numerous external and internal factors, political consensus has been reached in Yugoslavia on the necessity of solving current and development problems by applying up-to-date scientific and technological achievements, particularly through the rapid development and maximal utilisation of domestic R&D capacities. The prevailing belief is that Yugoslavia does not have distinct comparative natural advantages which would make it possible to offset for the negative consequences of a low level of technological development.

The three basic principles of scientific and technological policy (see Chapter II) will be maintained within the intended re-organisation of the economy and society.

Agreement has been reached to make the Yugoslav economy market-oriented. This implies the abandonment of the practice of absorbing losses of non-competitive entreprises. Competitive technological development of enterprises will be a condition *sine qua non* for their maintenance and success on local and foreign markets. Policies implying that the Yugoslav economy can remain competitive only through low prices of domestic resources and labour are being abandoned. They are being replaced by a philosophy of economic restructuring, enabling Yugoslavia's industry to reach a satisfactory level of international competitiveness. The will to master new technologies is gaining ground in Yugoslav society. The objective is to make domestic scientific research organisations much more efficient in mastering acceptance, adaptation and diffusion of new technologies. The conviction prevails that such a policy, together with a simultaneous acceptance of economic criteria of efficiency, will provide better results and create conditions for a long-term, effective economic and social development.

Yugoslavia's public at large and political leaders are increasingly convinced of the necessity to create and develop small innovative organisations. Business risk, inherent in technical change, is accepted as an intrinsic part of production and management. The creation of new jobs and solving of difficult problems of unemployment seem possible only by creating new organisations and by developing and introducing new products and processes.

New generations are less inclined to rely on stable employment and routine jobs, preferring to take initiatives and risks in mastering new developments. They are also more mobile and willing to introduce great changes in political, economic and work behaviour.

However, these new trends are still hampered by the resistance of particular interest groups which, in order to preserve their positions, even on irrational grounds, prevent full utilisation of existing scientific and technological capacities and development of new ones. This resistance to the current changes and to application of new solutions within enterprises is still very strong.

2. Major new initiatives

Reflecting the positive political commitment in science and technology, the Federal Assembly adopted in 1986 the Resolution on Science and Technology Development in Yugoslavia. This Resolution provides the legal basis for creating a system of mechanisms for promoting science and technology and for their relations with other economic and social sectors.

All important bodies, organisations and institutions adopted the agreement which set out the principles of technological development strategy in Yugoslavia. A special board of the Federal Assembly was set up in order to conduct and control the implementation of this agreement.

The Federal Committee for Science and Technology was established in 1986. This agency of the Federal Government adopted the Draft Strategy of Technological Development for Yugoslavia, outlined in 1985 by the former Federal Committee for Energy and Industry (no federal government agency for science and technology existed at that time). Public discussion of this initiative is under way.

Science and technology agencies, the SCI for Science and the Chambers of Commerce of the federal units are financing studies on policies and strategies for scientific and/or technological development in the federal units. Up to now, the following studies have been published:

- *Strategy for scientific-technological development of the Republic of Serbia to the year 2000* (project in co-operation with the OECD Technical Co-operation Service). Public discussion is now under way and the strategy will in due course be adopted in the Assembly of the Republic of Serbia;
- *Strategy for technological development in the Republic of Slovenia*, part of the project " Slovenia in the year 2000"; and
- *Basic problems of technological development of the Republic of Bosnia and Herzegovina up to the year 2000.*

Other studies under way include:

- *Strategy of technological development in Montenegro;*
- *Basic trends of technological development in Vojvodina;*
- *Bases for long-term development of science and strategy of technological development of the Republic of Croatia;*
- *Strategy for technological development of Kosovo;* and
- *Strategy for long-term development of scientific research activities in the Republic of Macedonia up to the year 2000.*

The Strategy of Technological Development of Yugoslavia was discussed in the Federal Assembly in the first half of 1987. This Strategy defines basic criteria for the evaluation of technologies and the selection of priorities; mechanisms for implementation of the Strategy; relations between this Strategy and those of the federal units; technological development of infrastructural and other basic technological systems; and international scientific co-operation.

In addition to this Strategy, measures for the support of technological development have also been adopted, including 29 measures with the following basic targets:

- Eliminating obstacles to efficiency of the country's science and technology;
- Improving the efficiency of scientific research and developments institutions, especially those developing new technologies (products and/or processes);
- Establishing good co-ordination and international scientific and technological co-operation; and
- Enhancing Yugoslavia's scientific and technological infrastructure.

One of the most important measures is the creation of the Fund for stimulation of technological development at federal level. This Fund is not financed from the government budget, but has its own permanent source of income. In 1987 the available funds should amount to the equivalent of $90 million.

The Strategy for Technological Development of Yugoslavia, measures aimed at supporting science and technology, strategies of scientific and technological development of the federal units and other similar programmes (sectoral technological development policy, large organisations, etc.) are all based on the economic interest of enterprises and other users of technology. The role of government (Federal and republic) and their agencies is to create a favourable social and economic conditions and climate, and to inform, assist and co-ordinate if and when necessary. Government does not and will not have any normative or coercive role in the development of science and technology.

The Association of SCI for Science in Yugoslavia has set up a plan for development of R&D activities for the period 1986-90, which has been submitted for final revision and was due to be enacted in the first half of 1987. This Association initiates, organises, finances and follows up three categories of projects: federal projects, financed by all members of the Association and formulated for their needs; joint projects formulated for the needs of not less than four out of the nine members; and co-ordinated projects, formulated for the needs of not less than two members of the Association.

The following federal-level research projects, strongly related to technological development, are under way:

- a system of biomedical information;
- development of scientific information system in the area of self-management in Yugoslavia;
- a programme of development of the system of scientific and technological informations in Yugoslavia up to the year 2000; and
- a strategy of technological development of Yugoslavia up to the beginning of the 21st century.

The following projects are in the stage of preparation:

- increased food production;
- genetic engineering and biotechnology;
- anthropological characteristics of children and young people in Yugoslavia;
- research on the utilisation, protection and improvement of the Adriatic Sea up to the year 2000;
- microelectronics and optoelectronics;
- reduction of electric power and energy losses in the electro-energy system of the country;
- flexible manufacturing systems;
- socially owned enterprises under the Associated labour act;
- the economic system of Yugoslavia;
- education and the scientific and technological development of Yugoslavia;
- introduction of robotics;

- protection of the human environment, water and air;
- new materials;
- seismology and earthquake engineering;
- bases for long-term development of research activities in Yugoslavia;
- development of chemical-technological and biotechnological food processing; and
- a geomorphological map of Yugoslavia.

In addition to the political spheres, many professional organisations are paying great attention to science and technology development. Besides their role as important sources of information, these organisations have a large influence on public opinion. They have initiated important changes in the system of values (higher social ranking of creativity and innovative behaviour), with the aim of improving the status of technological personnel in the economy, encouraging young people to study in the technical, biotechnical and natural science faculties, and promoting stronger reliance of government and its agencies on the opinions and proposals of researchers and experts, etc.

International scientific and especially technological co-operation will be considerably developed with particular emphasis on the programme of scientific and technological co-operation with the European Community. Measures are being studied to promote the return of Yugoslav researchers employed in other countries are encourage their active involvement in solving the problems encountered by domestic research organisations.

Each federal unit promotes its specific programmes, measures and implementation of scientific and technological development. For example, Slovenia has a programme for the training of "2 000 new researchers by 1990". The objective of this initiative is to finance, through the Slovenia Community for Science, the training of 2 000 young people for scientific work in institutes and faculties so as to renew the population of researchers and increase both the absolute and relative number of researchers in enterprises. In Serbia, a programme of scholarships for talented students has been established by the Serbian academy of sciences and arts (in natural sciences) and the University of Belgrade (for social sciences and humanities, etc.). This programme is financed by the Republic. Serbia plans to develop the large scientific research and education centre of Zvezdara (in the suburbs of Belgrade). A Centre for genetic engineering has also been set up, and the establishment of a Science and Technology Policy Research Centre is well under way. In Croatia, courses of computerisation of schools is under way and the possibility of opening science centres is under consideration, etc.

Under the long-term development plan at least 2.5 per cent of GDP (using the Yugoslav definition – see Chapter II) will be earmarked for R&D by the year 2000. Up to 1990 the percentage should reach at least 1.5 per cent of GDP (annual growth rate of 7 per cent), although the figure of 2 per cent would be much more in accordance with the role and tasks implied by R&D activities.

Serbia and Slovenia are planning for their R&D expenditures to reach 2 per cent of their GDP by 1990. For Yugoslavia as a whole, expenditure on R&D will probably reach 1.6 per cent of GDP by 1990 (as against 1 per cent at present).

3. Problems and prospects

The achievement of a planned and ambitious development of science and technology in Yugoslavia will meet considerable obstacles. Many problems will have to be solved, among which the most important are considered below.

Long-term policies for economic development and structural change have not yet been adopted by many enterprises. Short-term business operations do not generate a real demand for scientific and technological innovations. This is a major barrier which could (and probably will) be overcome in the near future by adopting changes in the socio-political and economic system.

Another limiting factor will be the co-ordination between production, R&D, education and other activities, particularly as to: synthesis and adoption of a national strategy of economic and technological development; efficient allocation of funds earmarked for science and technology; efficient use of the allocated funds and available research capacities; and especially effective transfer and diffusion of technology. Improvement of co-ordination depends also on changes on the behaviour of the socio-political system.

The traditional preference given by scientific research organisations, mainly in natural sciences, both in independent institutes and at universities for non-mission-oriented research without any plannning as regards orientation, choice of subjects, allocation of expenditures and time needed for carrying out research, makes the research system inefficient.

The need for engineers and personnel educated in the field of natural sciences has grown rapidly and is continuing to do so in industry, education and R&D activities. For the moment and for some time to come, there will be a shortage of electrical engineers, automation engineers, flexible system specialists, etc. Prospects for a favourable solution of this problem are not very good.

Highly talented graduates, outstanding young researchers and other qualified people very often take a temporary job in foreign laboratories and research centres. Attracted by wider research possibilities and far better research climates, they tend to prolong their temporary stay which frequently becomes permanent. This brain-drain of the most valuable scientific research potential cannot be prevented – all that can be done is to reduce it by the creation of better research conditions in Yugoslavia. There are good but limited prospects for this, so that the brain-drain problem will continue to be of a great importance to Yugoslavia up to the end of this century.

There are cases of well-developed and fruitful co-operation between the higher education system and industry, but a sizeable university potential is still not involved sufficiently in R&D activities. This problem can be solved successfully if the economic policy measures so far implemented make industry more interested in technological development, orienting faculties and higher education schools towards co-operation with industry.

In general, R&D units in enterprises are not sufficiently developed. It is planned that by the year 2000 the number of researchers employed in industry will account for 35-40 per cent of the total number of researchers in the country, instead of 20 per cent at present. This can be accomplished only if enterprises base their development on the optimum use on technology.

The difficulties that Yugoslavia has encountered so far in relation to its participation in international industrial R&D programmes and projects (e.g. Eureka, and some other programmes of the EEC, etc.) will constitute a considerable obstacle to development of new technologies.

The complex regulated and controlled international market of technologies and the great difficulties encountered in acquisition of competitive technologies from abroad are problems which will restrict, to a great extent, technological development in Yugoslavia.

The most serious and lasting problem to be solved before achieving a science and technology-based development of Yugoslavia's economy and society is the creation of a favourable climate for innovation, capable of generating, assessing, accepting and implementing all kinds of innovations: scientific, technological, organisational, social, cultural, etc. The creation of such a climate in Yugoslavia is largely a political and cultural problem. To solve this problem will require institutional, governmental and other measures.

GLOSSARY[1]

Basic organisation of associated labour
(osnovna organizacija udruzenog rada)

The fundamental form of association of labour in which workers directly and on equal terms realise their socio-economic and other self-management rights, and decide on other questions concerning their socio-economic status. A basic organisation of associated labour is formed for each unit of a work organisation which makes up a working whole (a plant, a technological unit, etc.) in which the results of joint labour can be expressed in terms of value on the market or within the work organisation concerned.

Delegate system
(delegatski sistem)

It is the groundwork upon which assemblies (commune, provincial, republic and federal) are constituted on the basis of collective delegations of organisations of associated labour, local communities and socio-political organisations. The delegate system ensures direct presence by working people in the assemblies, makes impossible political outvoting of one category of the population by another, and ensures functional linkage of short- and long-term interests of individual sections of society and of society as a whole. The delegate system is an institutionally new and special kind of link between self-management and government. It is the universal principle underlying Yugoslavia's entire socio-political system.

Free exchange of labour
(slobodna razmena rada)

A form of earning income in the basic organisations of associated labour which perform activities in the spheres of education, science, culture, health and social welfare or some other social activity. The income is realised by giving services of joint interest, directly and/or within the framework of self-managing communities of interest, from the income of other basic organisations, in accordance with the contribution made by their labour to the generation of value added in material production, the rise in the productivity of total social labour, and the development of society as a whole.

Income
(dohodak)

A part of society's total product which workers in basic organisations earn in monetary form as the social recognition of the results of their own and total social labour under conditions of the socialist mode of commodity production, and which they manage in basic organisations on the basis of their right to work with social resources; the part of the gross income after covering the value of all material resources used up in the process of reproduction (material costs) and of the permanent means of production and other instruments of labour (depreciation charges).

The net income is a part of income of basic organisation allocated for the personal incomes and collective consumption of workers, the promotion and expansion of the material base of labour and the creation and renewal of reserves in basic organisation and for ensuring the common and general conditions of labour and development of society.

Organization of associated labour
(organisacija udruzenog rada)

Denotes all forms of independent, self-managing organisations within which the workers engage in economic or other social activities with socially-owned means; forms of association set up on the basis of integration of the labour of workers who work with socially-owned means; in them the workers manage the labour and the business operations of the organisation and the affairs and means of social reproduction; they regulate their mutual labour relations, make decisions on the income they realise through various forms of the association of labour and the conception of "organisation of associated labour" is a general one which embodies the following concrete forms; basic organisation of associated labour, work organisation and complex organisation of associated labour. Organisations of associated labour were formerly designated by the words "enterprise" (applicable to the economy) and "institution" (applicable to non-economic activities).

Self-management agreements
(samoupravni sporazumi)

They are self-management acts adopted, on equal terms, by workers in organisations of associated labour and by workers in work communities, communities of interest and other self-managing organisations, with a view to regulating and co-ordinating their interests for purposes of a more efficient specialisation of production the pooling of labour and resources, and the formation of work and other organisations of associated labour. In this way the regulative and intermediary role of the state concerning relations among working people is curtailed. A self-management agreement is only binding on those who have signed or acceded to it.

Self-management communities of interest
(samoupravne interesne zajednice)

They are associations formed by working people directly or through their self-managing organisations and communities, with a view to satisfying their personal and collective needs. Their aim is to link the interests of those who use such services. In self-managing communities of interest users and renderers of services freely exchange their labour (by means of money as the common medium of exchange) to satisfy their needs. According to the Constitution, the assemblies of self-managing communities of interest in the sphere of education, science, culture, health and welfare are authorised to decide, together and on equal terms with the assemblies of the competent socio-political communities (communes, provinces, republics), on all matters falling within these spheres. There are also self-managing communities of interest in the field of housing construction, power production, water resources management, transport, etc.

Social compacts
(drustveni dogovori)

Social compacts are self-management enactments adopted, on equal terms, by organisations of associated labour and their associations, self-managing communities of interest and other self-managing organisations and communities, agencies of socio-political communities, trade unions and other socio-political and social organisations, by which the parties thereto regulate socio-economic and other relations of common concern, as well as relations of general concern to the community. The purpose of social compacts is to replace the state's role in the resolution of social contradictions and to ensure co-operation and solidarity in the economic and other spheres of life. Social compacts are binding upon the parties which have concluded or acceded to them, and must be in conformity with the Constitution and Statute.

Note

1. The following definitions are extracted from a more extended glossary presented in *Review of National Policies for Education – Yugoslavia*, OECD, Paris, 1981.

Part II

EXAMINERS' REPORT

This report has been prepared on the basis of information collected during a visit to the country which took place on 28th March-5th April 1987 and drawing on the General Report provided by the Yugoslav Authorities.

SUMMARY

General considerations

Yugoslavia is presently facing a major economic crisis characterised by a very high inflation rate (around 100 per cent a year), an increase in unemployment (approaching 15 per cent of the active population), and a large foreign debt (US$19 billion). This crisis is reducing the living standard of each citizen, giving rise to social problems and affecting the cohesion of the whole country constituted by extremely diverse Federal Units (Republics and Autonomous Provinces).

The current difficulties are largely due to a socio-economic system which is not sufficiently productive and which is not oriented towards quality production. The continued operation of loss-making enterprises (under the protection of local and regional interest groups) and the existence of mechanisms for the socialisation of these losses are major factors contributing to the poor performance of the Yugoslav economy.

Economic rules are changing at the world level. International competitiveness is increasingly determined by quality, productivity, efficiency, pervasive adoption of new technologies, attention to environment and natural resources and integration of economic sectors. These factors require a broad diffusion of knowledge throughout society where science and technology play a critical role.

While the role of science is important, its contribution to the economic recovery of Yugoslavia can be realised only in the longer term. More immediate impact can be obtained from changes of attitudes as regards quality and productivity, workforce motivation and development of good management practices. All these aspects are integral parts of a sound innovation policy.

The scientific and technological system

The scientific and technological system in Yugoslavia is excessively fragmented and most research activities lack the necessary "critical mass". Financing bodies, such as the Self-management Communities of Interest for Science, should attempt to focus their support on the most talented teams and the most interesting projects. More co-ordination among research efforts throughout the country is also necessary. In this context the establishment of the Federal Committee for Science and Technology, the elaboration of the national strategy for technological development, and the creation of the federal fund to stimulate technology (US$80 million) are good steps in the right direction.

It is advisable that financial support at the national level be primarily directed to supporting the development of national excellence centres, participation in international projects, and high quality industrial research closely related to market needs and technological areas where the country enjoys comparative advantages. Excessive bureaucracy and redistributive criteria should be eliminated in the administration of federal support.

Considerable efforts are required in education and training at all levels: primary, secondary and tertiary. A well-educated society, equipped with appropriate technical and managerial skills, should be the first priority of any development policy. The relative decrease of third level education expenditures at national level is a worrying trend which should be corrected. Radio, television and other media should be asked to intensify their efforts to offer a reliable picture of Yugoslavia as a nation making use of its science and technology talents for developing human welfare.

Other OECD countries should help in strengthening the scientific and technological potential of Yugoslavia. This may include help in developing its scientific information systems or excellence centres as well as a more open access to international technology projects (e.g. at European level). For their part Yugoslav organisations need to streamline conditions of co-operation, ensure continuity of effort, and agree on projects of national interest. It is also recommended that a better use be made of Yugoslav scientists working abroad, who can facilitate international co-operation.

The climate for innovation and economic growth

Low cost policy measures can significantly improve the climate for innovation and growth. Productivity gains and quality improvements can be obtained throughout the economy by publicising and drawing inspiration from most efficient enterprises. Absorption of foreign technology would be facilitated by clarification of conditions of technology transfer and joint ventures, as well as by reinforcement of licensing capabilities of Yugoslav enterprises. The establishment of free trade areas offers interesting opportunities for attracting advanced production and R&D facilities.

Plans to introduce a more market-led economy and to restructure or eliminate unprofitable enterprises will usefully contribute to an improvement in the climate for innovation and growth. Excessive bureaucracy, red tape and restrictive regulations must also be reduced. The intention to increase the maximum authorized number of employees for private small businesses should be implemented as soon as possible.

Meanwhile, without waiting for changes in the socio-economic framework, a number of actions could be undertaken on a much larger scale than is done at present: for instance, the development of local and regional offices for innovation to provide entrepreneurs with risk capital and needed assistance in technology, marketing, etc.; promotion of technological services such as design, software, engineering by appropriate organisations and small enterprises; and provision of management courses needed by industry, particularly through the use of the existing network of institutes and faculties in each Federal Unit.

Efforts should be focussed not only on manufacturing industry but also on other sectors. Progress is necessary in agriculture and food production in view of the diversity of the country's needs and comparative advantages enjoyed in certain fields. Considerable improvements are required in public services such as health care, transportation and telecommunications and can be developed through appropriate public procurement policies. Tourism development is probably the quickest way to yield foreign currency and should receive a high priority. Major progress in this area can be obtained at low cost, as illustrated by improvement of quality in hotel and tourist services.

Yugoslavia's principles: problems and opportunities

Policies and programmes for science, technology and innovation need to be considered within the context of those principles which form Yugoslavia's identity: multinationality, self-management and non-alignment. These principles, if carefully exploited, offer important opportunities for further development of the country.

As regards multinationality as basis of the federal organisation, the variety between the different peoples and units which constitute the whole nation can be an important asset, if properly integrated. Rather than choosing the way of separate development and economic autarky, each Federal Unit must identify its own role in developing further its strong points, including traditional activities, e.g. agriculture, craftmanship, tourism, etc. Joint approaches, e.g. in industrial ventures and training facilities, are recommended between the more advanced regions and the less advanced ones. For the latter regions, a massive effort should be pursued. Moreover, there is a need for unification between Federal Units as regards basic infrastructures for technological development such as telecommunication equipment, metrology, patents and technical standards. This would make sense in both economic and political terms.

The creative dimension of self-management, as the organisation principle of the Yugoslav economy and society, needs to be further developed. So far, self-management has been more concerned with the distribution of income. Recognition and development of creativeness at the shopfloor level is necessary, as well as delegation of responsibility to smaller groups within the "basic organisations of associated labour" through establishment of quality circles, better use of the "registers of innovators", etc., and appropriate financial incentives. There is also a need to accept delegation of responsibility upward, notably as regards day to day management of enterprises and organisations, which is difficult for workers' councils to undertake efficiently. In all cases competition should be encouraged as a key to improved efficiency and growth. Making self-management more creative and more efficient is fundamental for the survival of the present Yugoslav system.

The principle of non-alignment creates, in certain circles, a feeling of isolation or leads to excessive emphasis on technological self-sufficiency. But in developing its capacities of technology absorption in one hand and technology transfer in the other, Yugoslavia can become a "technology bridge" between the North and the South, the East and the West, particularly within the Mediterranean area.

Suggested policy actions

The final chapter of the report summarises the views of the Examiners with regard to key actions to be taken throughout the country, at all levels of the society from the bottom up to the top. This advice is presented under four headings: building of a knowledge-intensive economy, improving the country's technological performance, adapting the socio-institutional framework and internationalising Yugoslav science and technology.

Yugoslavia is generally aware of the gravity of the economic situation, has identified clearly the issues and has elaborated plans and strategies accordingly. It is important that *action* moves ahead rapidly at all levels.

I. INTRODUCTION

The information collected in meetings with the Federal Authorities in Belgrade, as well as during visits to the Republics and Autonomous Provinces has enabled the examining team to form a good picture of the present state of the scientific, technological and innovation policy of Yugoslavia. Visits to enterprises, research institutes and other organisations were highly interesting and took place in an atmosphere characterised by a widespread support for changes intended to create an efficient, knowledge-intensive society.

The General Report provided by the Yugoslav Authorities is very informative on the research system and analyses in depth the scientific and technological situation. Reasons for the present difficulties of the country are well investigated, emphasizing the relationships between economic development and scientific and technological capabilities. The Examiners have greatly appreciated this report for its analytical depth and intellectual honesty.

The Examiners' Report concentrates on essential problems and policy proposals. Selected examples illustrate how weak points can be reduced and strong ones reinforced in future policies.

The Report contains five chapters. The first formulates some general considerations on the economic and political situation of the country and the role of science and technology in economic development. The second Chapter discusses the scientific and technological system and ways to improve its functioning. The third Chapter comments on the climate for innovation and economic growth and ways to make this climate more favourable. The fourth Chapter places science, technology and innovation policies within the context of the principles of multinationality, self-management and non-alignement which form the country's identity[1]. The fifth and concluding Chapter summarises the policy orientations provided throughout the Report with a view to guiding future policies.

II. GENERAL CONSIDERATIONS

1. At the cross-roads

Yugoslavia is beautiful and diverse both in its landscapes and its peoples. Yugoslavs are fond of relating that their country has seven international boundaries, six Republics and two Autonomous Provinces, six nations, four principal languages, three main religions and two alphabets. In this diversity lie some of Yugoslavia's strengths and some of its weaknesses.

Since the Second World War Yugoslavia has achieved a remarkable development based on a unique socialistic policy approach. From a situation where the country was practically devastated, it has been possible to build up a non-aligned industrial federation, differing very much from the pre-war, relatively poor society based mainly on agriculture. In the late thirties, three quarters of the population were dependent on agriculture. Nowadays the proportion is one fifth. Less than six per cent of pre-war exports were finished goods. Now the proportion is over 60 per cent. Up to the mid-1970s the country enjoyed high growth in GDP and productivity.

This impressive record in quantitative terms, however, has had an adverse side. The economy, beset by fundamental qualitative weakenesses, has been encountering increasing difficulties in coping with major changes affecting the world economy since the mid-1970s: i.e. slow growth, fiercer international competition and rapid technical change.

The country is now suffering from a very high inflation rate (around 100 per cent a year), an export-import deficit and decreasing productivity. These features are particularly worrying in the light of high investments in and imports of technology, made especially in the late 1970s and financed to a great extent by international loans, causing the development of a considerable international debt (US$19 billion).

The problems of Yugoslav industry are largely due to the market situation in which it operates: a situation characterised by a limited foreign competition and a socio-economic context which significantly inhibits internal competition. Enterprises are protected by local interest groups so that regional aspirations and other factors create barriers against the overall development needs of the country. In the course of the review visit, different sources indicated that as many as 25 per cent of the enterprises were loss making and would in practice have gone bankrupt, if they had not had the right to draw funds from "joint reserves". Thus the fragmentation of the economy and the socialisation of losses seem to be important factors contributing to its current difficulties.

The same factors largely explain the high inflation rate. The recent OECD Economic Survey of Yugoslavia[2] identified as major causes of inflation: a high degree of market segmentation and the associated lack of competition; the absence of financial discipline of enterprises and the related lack of economic efficiency; and insufficient monetary control over the growth of nominal income and demand associated with negative real interest rates, unchecked growth of inter-enterprise credit, and failure to take into account the implications of large holdings of foreign currency deposits by households.

Policy responses at federal level include strong deflationary measures to cope with the most immediate problems and a "Long term Stabilisation Programme" based on the intention to develop a more market-led economy. Restrictive financial measures, notably wage and salary freezes or reductions, have led to social difficulties. A number of strikes have recently taken place in various parts of the country.

Current difficulties have led to a questioning of aspects of the basic organisation of the society that Yugoslavia pioneered, i.e. self management and the related decentralised decision-making system. The society is constructed from the bottom up – from the "basic organisations of associated labour" – to more complex organisations at local, regional and republican level. A system of delegation is supposed to allow for the expression of the interests of all those involved in a given area of activity and for a broad participation of all employees in the process of planning, decision-making and management of working organisations (i.e. enterprises).

The difficult economic situation also creates tensions between the regions which constitute the nation as a whole. The variety in the economic base, cultural attitudes and infrastructure and, last but not least, demographic trends, is considerable (see Table 6 of the General Report). The GDP per capita of the Republic of Slovenia, the richest Federal Unit, is seven times that the Province of Kosovo (of which the fertility rate is 26 per 1 000, while the average for Yugoslavia is 8 per 1 000).

A major consequence of this difference in development is that the economic crisis and its implications – e.g. the reduction of purchasing power – are not perceived with the same intensity, thus leading to important differences of appreciation as regards the nature and depth of reforms and changes required throughout the society.

2. Science, technology and economic development

Yugoslav society, in general, has accepted that science and technology play an essential role in future development. This is clearly seen from the rapid growth in the number of research units and researchers, enrolments in universities, and the efforts made by industry to improve its technological level. A Federal Committee (Ministry) for Science and Technology has recently been established (end of 1986).

The national scientific effort can be characterised by several input indicators including the national expenditure for R&D and manpower. The figures are 1 000 researchers per one million inhabitants and 0.9 per cent of GNP for R&D, approximately one fourth of this for fundamental research. According to certain estimations, Yugoslavia produces about 0.2-0.25 per cent of world scientific knowledge. The productivity would hence be comparable with that of Spain, Ireland and Greece and above that of Bulgaria and Romania[3].

Science is a long term investment for the progress of the society and not an immediate tool for industrial development. New products are seldom the results of a direct line from science via R&D and production to marketing. On the contrary, in market-based economies, market pull is a key factor, naturally combined with technology push. This push may have a close relation to science, as illustrated by the development of microprocessors or genetic engineering. But the scientific results forming the fundamental background for technological development are generally well known, years before the appearance of new technologies and products.

The process of technological development is complex. Like football, it requires good team-work among capable actors who, each with his special skills, are able to make the combinations which lead to the goal.

As well as expertise in technical areas and in management, quality control, industrial design, marketing, etc. an important factor is the climate for technological development and innovation.

There is no doubt that one of the critical factors in Yugoslav development is the low motivation for innovative action. This is partly due to a lack of economic resources and of access to adequate technology, but it may be more a result of an economic climate with little effective market competition and incentives, and a lack of modern management skills.

These factors are critical as there is a mistaken tendency to think that promotion of science and technology is the dominant factor for economic and industrial development. We find that it is essential to improve scientific work in Yugoslavia. But it is even more important that general management be improved and motivation of the workforce be increased. These steps are vital to ensure that the right decisions are made when new technology is introduced, and to avoid losses caused by low productivity and bad quality. Inefficient management, and a framework allowing enterprises to continue to exist without real restructuring can be regarded as the most important reasons for the disappointing results in Yugoslav development during recent years.

The General Report rightly emphasizes quality as the distinctive element of the emergent phase of advanced economies: from this point of view the Yugoslav system is obviously lagging and should radically improve its production structure and adapt it to the quality requirements of international markets.

There is a widespread belief that productive quality and the scientific and technological content are substantially equivalent values, and that the low international competitiveness of Yugoslav products is due to the inadequate technological level of products and processes. Our feeling is that the reality is quite different: the low quality of average Yugoslav production may be due less to a low technological content than to insufficient attention paid to the final user's needs. In an advanced society, knowledge is the critical success resource: the scientific know-how is just one element in the necessary knowledge.

If knowledge is the key-tool in achieving product quality, many other elements of knowledge – besides science – have then to be considered: awareness of customer requirements, aesthetics, reliability and durability of products. Such considerations have direct consequences in terms of policy. Policy measures should not be exclusively oriented towards science and technology but also towards these key elements, and for instance, towards the development of design and business schools and the motivation and training of basic workers on the shop floor.

III. THE SCIENTIFIC AND TECHNOLOGICAL SYSTEM

1. Strengths and weaknesses

The organisation of science in Yugoslavia combines both strong and weak points. These have not very much changed since the first (and only previous) OECD Science Policy Review made in 1974[4]. In short, they can be summed up as follows:

The strengths are:

i) Widespread awareness that science and technology are important success factors for the development of a modern society; this is felt at all levels: government, industries, trade-unions, universities, etc. This attention towards science is expressed through ambitious development plans concerning R&D expenditures at a federal level, by single republics and by individual firms. There is also the consciousness of the necessity to combine a quantitative growth of the research effort with qualitative improvements concerning staff, equipment, planning and management in research structures.

ii) Existence of mechanisms to ensure that the voice of science and technology is heard in the centres of political, social and economic debate: through the Self-Management Communities of Interest for Science (SCIS) where "users" and "producers" of science join together[5]. Thus, science can find expression all over the territory. Although this specific Yugoslav mechanism presents some weaknesses that we shall discuss later, its positive long-term effect on national culture cannot be overestimated, in view of a widespread opening towards science and technology as well as of the integration of research work in other kinds of work.

iii) Autonomy of universities and independent institutes. The Yugoslav system is apparently full of constraints; but, indeed, research units enjoy a degree of autonomy in their operations including: organisational means, acquisition of funds, aggregation and disaggregation of institutes, forms of exerting power (self-management or more traditional forms), types of activity (basic research, applied research, consulting and services to industry, governments, SCIS and foreign bodies as well as even production of advanced technologies). Any future reorganisation of the R&D system should maintain and support this general flexibility which allows development possibilities for the most effective institutes.

iv) Wide diffusion of contacts, collaboration, and interaction of all kinds between industry and university/independent institutes. Of course, there are examples of unsatisfactory collaboration, but, generally speaking, the will to co-operate is widely present on both sides and there are no apparent major institutional or bureaucratic obstacles to such co-operation.

v) High level of scientific and technological education of scientists, engineers and technicians as compared to the level of economic development of the country. A further positive element is the frequency of international contacts by the most dynamic institutes. Among these, we were impressed by major independent bodies such as Josef Stefan Institute (Ljubljana), Ruder Boskovic Institute (Zagreb), Mihajlo Pupin and Boris Kidric Institutes (Belgrade).

The weak points are:

i) Quantitative insufficiency of the global R&D effort in the country: the will expressed at federal level and by single Republics to consider science and technology as a priority and to invest more in the research sector are obvious, but the economic development level of the country and the current crisis do not facilitate the realisation of larger ambitions in this respect.

ii) Fragmentation of the R&D effort: the Yugoslav organisational structure allows the creation and diffusion of a great number of R&D units throughout the society. The negative aspect is not due to the number of institutes but to the fact that often they lack "critical mass", that is to say, their size is smaller than the minimum efficiency threshold. Even more serious than the fragmentation of research structures is the fragmentation of research projects, which also occurs within some big institutes (both independent institutes and universities). The situation is such that most projects are small and short-term in nature, whilst larger projects are frequently under-resourced and therefore too ambitious.

iii) Short-term directions of R&D projects: as a result of many factors (such as typical Yugoslav decision-making mechanisms, fragmentation of both research structures and projects, serious economical problems, etc.) it seems extremely difficult to launch large long-term research projects, aiming at structural changes in the country. This situation is then worsened by the self-reliant independent spirit in the Republics which affects the development and success of projects on a federal scale. Even an original and interesting initiative such as the Register of Innovators, used in almost all firms, favours small technical improvements proposed by single individuals, rather than the development of more sophisticated and fruitful proposals elaborated by teams of workers.

iv) Lack of a scientific and technological policy at a central level, as a consequence of the highly decentralised decision-making political system. The lack of planning is particularly negative regarding the following issues:

- creation of "excellence centres" for most advanced technologies: the dimension and the economic level of Yugoslavia allows only one or two such centres for each advanced sector and require that they play the role of "lighthouse" and "reference point" for the rest of the country;
- provision of core technological services such as standards, metrology, information, patents, etc.;
- ambitious plans for the country's modernisation as regards, for example telecommunications, management of natural resources, environment control, etc.

v) The lack of a central scientific and technological policy has prevented industrial research from having specific directions towards targets of general interest for the country: up to now, there has been little incentive for industrial research, both in general terms and in specific sectors. Industries self-finance almost completely their R&D efforts which are made with little consideration to the overall planning process and global needs of the country.

2. The need for co-ordination

Repeatedly and in all meetings with republican and provincial authorities, we were reminded that there was, up to very recently, no science and technology policy at the federal level. Not only each Republic or Province but also each major municipality and institute tries to define its own sphere of science and technology policy without paying much attention to what is done in other places. Most frequently the reasons given as a justification for this situation are historical development and principles of self-management.

These principles give a major role to "users of science" in a totally decentralised structure. The way of financing research in Yugoslavia is rather unique in the sense that the users, either through direct contracts or through the Self-Management Communities of Interest for Science, are responsible for around 90 per cent of the funding (see Table 15 of the General Report).

It is very positive that industry and other users of R&D participate in research financing, but this involvement will only be successful where appropriate R&D strategies and projects are established. This may be the case in the more advanced industries and enterprises, but it is certainly not in traditional sectors and smaller firms. Further, it must be admitted that it is very difficult to obtain a consensus to support R&D in other firms, for risky projects and long-sighted research programmes of a fundamental nature.

Similar problems might be linked to the funding from the Self-management Communities of Interest for Science (SCIS), as there appears to be a tendency to spread the funding as broadly as possible among the applicants rather than supporting the most highly qualified projects. It is also an open question whether the co-operation between science and society is functioning as expected. The SCIS seem dominated by the scientists while the users lack the qualification and interest for expressing clearly their needs. When people are really motivated as regards the nature of the service provided, they become much more active and demanding, as illustrated by the Communities of Interest for Education. It is generally agreed that these function quite well, because people, whatever their job or status in the society, are keen to see their children properly educated.

Many problems must be solved before this decentralised process of decision making in R&D funding may function efficiently. The problems of lack of co-ordination and formulation of long term objectives and strategies will be difficult to overcome. The presence of many bodies discussing R&D policy at all levels does not necessarily mean that optimal choices are made. It is generally admitted that research co-operation between teams or institutes throughout the country, or even within a Republic, is far below a desirable and efficient level. This is a major barrier to undertaking bigger research projects and leads to the fragmentation and dequalification of the research potentials. R&D efforts lead too often to results of minor interest for the Yugoslav society, and simply to a formal qualification for the researcher, in the form of a PhD or a similar diploma. The decentralised structure is also a barrier for participation in advanced international projects.

It is thus advisable to attempt to establish better co-ordination of the structure and policy of Yugoslav research. The human research potential is so considerable that much more ambitious research activities might be established and more original technological developments made than has been the case up to now.

In this context, we consider the establishment of the Federal Committee for Science and Technology as an important step towards more co-ordination, as well as the Draft Strategy for Technological Development prepared by the Committee and the establishment of the federal fund to finance technology projects of national interest (US$80 million per year, i.e. one third of the current national R&D expenditures).

However the calculation mechanism of federal incentives seems very complicated and it can render the bureaucracy for the approval of research proposals rather difficult. Complexity of access to federal money will inevitably favour large companies which have the structures, relationships and expertises to deal with bureaucratic procedures, whereas smaller companies will give up; an effect observed in all OECD countries. Larger supports by the Federal Government would be desirable[6], provided that any return to bureaucratisation of research is avoided. Moreover it is absolutely essential that redistributive considerations be totally excluded in the selection process of projects and allocation of money. The only criteria should be scientific and technological excellence, export orientation, etc.

Important initiatives have been taken at the level of the Republics – e.g. in Slovenia, Bosnia-Herzegovina and Serbia – to increase their R&D expenditures, to support new technologies, or to elaborate long term technological programmes, etc. These efforts could lead to exchange of views and to more co-operation with a view to avoiding wasteful duplication and facilitating the realisation of the federal technological strategy.

3. Research priorities

It is not surprising that the issue of the balance between basic and applied research was raised repeatedly in the course of our visit. A view which was frequently expressed was that Yugoslavia needs to devote more resources to basic research, and that a policy of concentrating more resources in basic research was the best way forward. We do not concur with this view. Only the largest economies in the world can devote large resources to all areas of basic research. The more advisable policy for smaller countries appears to be rather to direct resources to key areas and to the most talented scientists.

The improvement of a national network of highly qualified R&D institutions should have a high priority. This approach would aim at establishing internationally-oriented centres of excellence which might be nuclei for basic research, thus escaping the risk of fragmenting research which is obvious in the existing highly decentralised situation. Priority should be given to R&D institutions which have already demonstrated talents and good results and have the ability to present projects of high interest for the Yugoslav society. The greater part of R&D resources should be specifically directed towards achieving and sustaining economic growth, which is, in turn, the necessary condition to release further funds for more basic research activities.

It is interesting, in this context, to consider the success of the Maize Research Institute near Belgrade. This is a highly specialised research organisation for maize improvement. Its principal activities include the development of maize hybrids for different agro-ecological conditions; the development of crop-management systems; the utilisation of maize in animal feeds and industrial processing; and the production, handling and marketing of certified hybrid seed maize. The major results to date include the development of over 100 maize hybrids; scientific and technical co-operation with about 60 countries and an average annual production of hybrid seed maize of 35 000 tons. A noteworthy aspect of this institute, apart from its organisation and profitability, was its co-operation in research with such major international bodies as the Max Planck Institute. The co-operation project with Max Planck in the field of genetic research enabled the Maize Research Institute to build and develop on the results of expensive basic research carried out at the Max Planck, with beneficial results for both institutes.

As regards the monitoring of basic research, throughout the OECD region there is increasing application of bibliometric methods (publications and citations in international scientific journals), as a supplement to established peer reviews. In addition, greater use is being made of foreign experts in peer review procedures. By adopting a similar approach and by investing in international top scientists as leaders of scientific research units, Yugoslavia will get a better return on its investment in basic research. General networking and co-operation between top scientists in each field can be promoted through joint projects by supporting these projects through federal funding.

As regards the monitoring and control of applied technological research, it is important to pay special attention to the usefulness and the probable outcome of an applied technological research project, trying to link it with the ultimate customer and with international marketing, whenever possible. It is clear in the Yugoslav situation that the general principle of basing technological research on users' needs is broadly applied, in view of the particular financing structure of the research system. The problem comes with the fact that the users' requirements are often quite low. As regards enterprises' demands, more than one research manager enunciated the problem as follows: "Research laboratories are directed in their work by enterprises which are themselves not market-led". It is inevitable that, when Yugoslav enterprises are competing more openly in the market, the funding of R&D will gradually be re-directed towards the development of products for identified market niches and this will result in more concentrated investments in vital projects.

It is also highly advisable to consider areas of natural advantage. Each country has its natural advantages and traditional strengths, which represent for it the best opportunities for attaining and sustaining a slice of the world market. Some of Yugoslavia's natural strengths and potential for development lie in the tourism, forestry and agricultural product sectors (see below III.5). Evidence also abounds of significant strength in heavy engineering areas, for example the railway from Belgrade to the Adriatic port of Bar is a remarkable achievement, cutting its way through formidable mountain barriers, necessitating over 100 tunnels and 230 bridges.

Recent years have also witnessed the increase in exports of heavy capital goods such as complete power generating and industrial plants with enterprises such as Energoinvest (Sarajevo), mechanical and electrical engineering with UNIS (Sarajevo), electronics with ISKRA (Ljubljana), Electronska Industrja (Belgrade), and Nikolas Tesla (Zagreb). All these large industrial complexes, largely export oriented, report an investment in R&D up to 10 to 15 per cent of their "social income" (i.e. salaries plus capital amortization), an amount comparable with similar advanced industries in Western Europe and United States.

4. Industry-university linkages

A fundamental element for economic and technological development is a highly educated and open-minded population. Although we did not have opportunity to look at this topic in depth, we feel the need of providing some comments on this subject, and especially on the linkages between the education and industrial sectors.

As regards second-level education, we were informed on more than one occasion that there was a need to strengthen the teaching of science and mathematics at second-level. Other criticisms we met with were that the curriculum was overloaded and too much focussed on working-life oriented subjects. These views are reflected in the 1981 OECD Review of

National Policies for Education in Yugoslavia, where the examiners, when discussing the second-level curriculum, expressed a fear that "if such subjects loom too large... they will compromise the intention to defer choices by leading too many students into too early a specialisation"[7].

As regards third-level education, we encountered a number of examples of close co-operation and consultation between large industrial enterprises and their neighbouring universities. In particular we were impressed by initiatives taken in Bosnia-Herzegovina where several large enterprises had very active links with the university system, and had financially supported the establishment of new faculties and the education of scholarship students. In addition, R & D personnel in these concerns also lectured at university institutes. These close relationships did not, however, reflect the norm. The examiners were told, more than once, that industry did not have the people to understand and liaise with university researchers. In this respect, the "Slovenia 2000" initiative aiming at placing 2000 young graduates in industry after a two year stay in research institutes, largely paid by the Republic's government seems excellent and has already yielded positive results.

It would appear that there is room for closer collaboration between the Self-Management Communities of Interest for Education and the Self-Management Communities of Interest for Science on questions relating to the numbers of graduates required in the science and engineering fields. We were informed repeatedly, both in industry and in independent research institutes that there is a shortage in the supply of production engineers and specialists in information technology.

Another aspect of the scarcity problem relates to the emigration of some of the best graduates. The best way to curtail this, of course, is the provision of more attractive working conditions in Yugoslav industry. These conditions relate not only to pay and incentives but to the need for good laboratory and equipment facilities. The resolution of some of these problems also lies in the establishment of a better general climate and a more efficient economy together with a rationalisation of resources and the possibility of providing better rewards in successful enterprises. That would help also in reducing an important internal "brain drain" taking the form of highly educated students accepting unskilled jobs in order to survive. In Slovenia for instance, we have been told that only 30 per cent of graduates are working at the professional level for which they have been trained.

These problems of both internal and external brain drain have led some to question the need to invest in education. On the contrary, we believe that the education effort should be intensified. The share of GDP spent on university education is apparently decreasing. From 1980 to 1984 it fell from 0.74 to 0.52 per cent. The number of graduate students has also decreased. The decline in the number of graduates in natural and technical sciences is worrying (see Table 13 of the General Report).

5. International co-operation

We were impressed by the widespread desire to establish deeper contacts with fellow researchers internationally. In more than one instance, there was a feeling of a dearth of knowledge about corresponding research in more advanced countries. Many professors and researchers have studied and lectured overseas. Maintaining a high research standard is a prerequisite for international co-operation which is based on exchange of knowledge and is not a one-way traffic.

A number of research teams, notably in the best institutes, are well plugged into European networks such as the European Science Foundation and programmes such as COST (EEC). Some difficulties have been encountered with certain projects. They have not been due to the insufficient quality of the research teams, but rather to the general economic situation leading to financial restrictions on travel, the impossibility of acquiring the necessary advanced equipment, etc.

The Yugoslav Plan for the development of scientific research activities for the period 1986-90 includes the topic "Programme of development of scientific research information in SFR Yugoslavia up to 2000". OECD countries may assist in implementing this programme by facilitating access to data bases, providing information on research projects in priority fields, etc.

It might be advantageous too to improve the scientific and technological relations with the EEC and to participate – with an appropriate status – in some transnational projects, like BRITE (manufacturing technologies), ESPRIT (information technologies), RACE (communication equipment). Yugoslavia has also expressed the wish to participate in EUREKA. Whether it might benefit from this participation is a more open question as this programme is still in an early phase. Up to now there has been relatively little opportunity for participation by SMEs and enterprises without strong R&D units in advanced technologies.

Support by the international community can be decisive and is particularly important for projects directly related to the country's needs. A striking success story is the International Centre for Seismology and Earthquake Engineering at Skopje. The Centre was established in 1965 within the University "Kiril and Metody", on the recommendation of the United Nations International Consultative Board for the Repair and Reconstruction of the city of Skopje, and with the support of UNDP and UNESCO as well as of bilateral programmes (e.g. with the United States' National Science Foundation). While meeting immediate needs of reconstruction, the Centre has created conditions for continuous progress in research, established a strong staff of scientists and engineers, and become a highly recognised institution at international level. The activities of the Centre range from post-graduate education to fundamental and applied research, as well as to consultancy for international organisations, foreign governments and companies. Some 90 per cent of its income is derived from contracts, mainly at international level.

Helping in the establishment of centres of a similar level in other areas, e.g. agriculture, has encountered difficulties in reaching agreements between Republics regarding where such centres should be located. Further progress in international co-operation depends on mutual efforts of both Yugoslavia and the international community.

IV. THE CLIMATE FOR INNOVATION AND ECONOMIC GROWTH

1. Productivity and quality in industry

Industry in Yugoslavia has continuously grown since the Second World War. In the period 1973-85 industrial employment increased from 1.6 to 2.5 million: a much higher growth rate than in any other OECD country. Indeed the tendency in many OECD countries has been the opposite, i.e. a decrease in industrial employment. This record is partly explained by the fact that Yugoslavia was poorly industrialised, and a fast increase in industrial production was a key element in developing the economy.

The natural resources of the country are relatively diversified. They include a natural base for the production of steel, aluminium, other metals and various chemicals, forest and agricultural products as well as energy resources, i.e. coal, water power and, in limited quantities, oil. As a consequence Yugoslav industry is rather differentiated but, at the same time, characterised by a large proportion of enterprises based on production of raw materials and a small proportion with high added value products. The economy is dominated by large industrial groups operating in heavy sectors (mechanical, petrochemical, metallurgical, etc.), mining and commodity products (tobacco, cereals, etc.). There is a lack of small and medium-sized companies that are flexible, technology-based and export oriented.

In the late 1970s and early 1980s the situation deteriorated considerably and led to the Long Term Economic Stabilisation Programme of 1983. High priority is given to a quality based development in all sectors, to enhance business efficiency, productivity and accelerated progress based primarily on the country's own resources. If these courageous intentions are translated into efficient programmes of action, there is a fair chance of witnessing sound development. But much resistance has to be overcome, and some dogmatism must be countered. In the light of what we experienced and observed during our visits to enterprises we would like to make more specific comments.

Regarding productivity, greater profit might be obtained with simple changes. Some problems, naturally, are related to the lack of incentives and absence of sanctions for staff who do not fulfil basic requirements for work performance. This and the possibility to continue running loss-making enterprises year after year are severe impediments to the vital improvement of productivity. As an example, let us mention a paper factory with 2 000 workers, which has never been profitable and appears, compared to mills with a similar capacity in Scandinavia, remarkably overstaffed. No decisive initiatives have been taken to change this situation.

Another factor influencing productivity is the generally lax attitude to repair and maintenance. It is obvious, when visiting enterprises – and cities – that too little is done in the field of systematic maintenance, cleaning of work places, etc. Too much neglect and waste is observed. These remarks indicate that progress in large measure does not depend on elaborate science and technology or big investments, but on a change of attitudes. Greater efficiency cannot be achieved just by installing new technology, if basic requirements for its maintenance and running are not fulfilled.

A large proportion of Yugoslav industry is characterised by low quality, low priced and low value-added products. These products often are sold in a protected local market or exported at a loss. A precondition for improving industrial performance is a massive increase in quality and a reduction of waste caused by lack of continuous quality control. The introduction of "quality circles" has been tried, but apparently without much effort, in spite of the fact that the self management system should be a very sound base for such an approach, as commented later (Chapter IV, Section 3).

Traditional industries, e.g. furniture, clothing, agricultural machinery, etc., might benefit much from giving more attention to industrial design and product development. Experience in Denmark, Finland and Italy shows that design is a decisive factor in international competition. It is difficult to find Yugoslav products characterised by exceptional quality design. The remarkable capabilities and creativity of the Yugoslav Modern School of Architecture have proved to be particularly successful in the building sector, but they have not yet affected industrial design and fashion in the same way. One exception is the world famous ski factory ELAN, located in northern Slovenia, which has also demonstrated a remarkable ability to market its products in a very professional way: an example which should inspire the whole of Yugoslav industry[8].

Quality is improved by close co-operation with the professional customers, who define their quality specifications and are often ready to assist sub-contractors in obtaining the quality needed. Especially for smaller and medium-sized companies, this is a way of improving quality and gaining a foothold on export markets. The Mihajlo Pupin Institute in Belgrade already adopts a quality monitoring role in respect of industrial products developed under licence from the Institute. When the Institute signs a contract with a manufacturer, the contract stipulates that the manufacture must start within a specified period of time. If the factory fails to do this, the Institute has the right to licence the production to another manufacturer. An important stipulation in all contracts is that the performance of the product must be comparable with, or better than, similar products on the world market. This quality is guaranteed by the Institute.

Contracts with foreign customers can be also an important stimulus. Finland has recently ordered the steel hulls for two big passenger ferryboats from the shipyards in Split. The ships will be finished by the Finnish company Wärtsilä. The hulls are worth roughly US$50 million. This delivery by Yugoslav shipbuilders is not based on sophisticated technology, but on the belief of the buyer that Yugoslav workers can do the welding job well, and keep to the delivery time.

R&D, at a high level, is concentrated in a few advanced enterprises. These firms are not the problem. It is the many non science-based firms, practically without any R&D, which have to change their strategies. It is not realistic to propose that all enterprises should establish their own R&D units but, at a minimum, they should establish a product development function, possibly in close contact with R&D institutes or faculties which can provide the expertise needed – not only in appropriate technologies, but also in industrial design and marketing. Efforts in product development are vital for all industries including the more mature ones. The big "Kombinat Aluminuja Titograd" in Montenegro, having observed that selling aluminium blocks is no longer profitable, has developed a wide range of more value-added products such as different profiles, laminated foils, etc.

Co-operation with public authorities and customers is of particular relevance to industrial R&D. Many sources reported during our visit that authorities are bureaucratic and restrictive instead of being service minded. More generally, public customers are not acting as large buyers to support product development, as is seen in other countries, e.g. the United States, France, Germany, etc. where enterprises benefit considerably from government contracts which include a great proportion of R&D, and contribute to industrial competitiveness. But the specific way of financing R&D Yugoslavia prevents much progress in this area. It is also worthwhile to emphasize that the country has traditionally paid more attention to material goods and neglected the development of public services: health care, posts, telecommunications, mass media, etc.

2. Absorption of foreign technology

Major investments in foreign technology in the 1970s brought Yugoslav industry many steps forward. But these investments were costly in terms of foreign currency. The lack of domestic development and the decreasing possibilities for investment in foreign technology in the 1980s has probably widened the gap between the technological level of many Yugoslav enterprises and similar enterprises in Western Europe, USA and Japan. These trends lead certain segments of Yugoslav society to think that the country should attempt to move from the complete technological dependency characteristic of the past to an absolute technological autonomy. This seems to be too ambitious for a country like Yugoslavia, the more so since that path is not yet feasible for many other countries.

It is argued that too many restrictions from the exporting partner have been accepted, e.g. re-export restrictions. Furthermore it is said that enterprises have not made the efforts needed to develop new products and processes, but have contented themselves with imported technology. These arguments may be right in many cases, but we had the opportunity of visiting some advanced enterprises, e.g. "Nikolas Tesla" Telecommunicative Devices Industry in Zagreb where co-operation with an advanced foreign company (L.M. Ericsson), besides giving a good starting position, has been the base for domestic R&D and resulted in development of original new products. "Nikolas Tesla" now co-operates on an equal footing with L.M. Ericsson. This co-operative venture has received an order in China, valued as US$15 million, in open competition with large multinational firms. Similar experiences could be reported from other large industrial firms mentioned above.

Co-operation should not be, as in the past, dominated by the foreign partner, but have a framework where the partners work on an equal basis. A strategy of technological absorption should be developed. This strategy should focus on a careful selection of foreign technologies which would be the object of research efforts aimed at absorbing, adapting and integrating knowledge and, ultimately, providing a basis for autonomous improvements.

This strategy demands a greater capacity for technology transfer. With only a few exceptions, Yugoslav industry was, in the past, incapable of negotiating or exploiting licences to good effect. Technological transfer is a complex process, requiring a multidisciplinary negotiating team acting in an integrated manner, with competences of a financial, economical, legal, fiscal and technical nature. Universities and other schools should consider the establishment of technology transfer programmes in order to investigate the *modus operandi* of Yugoslav firms, identify their needs and put in hand consultancy and management training schemes.

The planned Free Trade Areas should facilitate the establishment of joint ventures with foreign-owned industries. These areas should be used not to establish traditional production, but to foster new, profitable enterprises which will inspire R&D and management practice in domestic firms.

Within this whole context can be put the question of Yugoslav scientists working abroad. A reverse policy of "brain-drain", aiming at encouraging the return to their country of emigrant scientists, is possible. Such a policy would probably be difficult to implement since scientists rarely find in their homeland the same working conditions as in more advanced countries. If they cannot be attracted back, it would be wise to develop a policy aiming at establishing good contacts between Yugoslav firms and universities and emigrant scientists, so that these will act as reference points for exchanges of information, advice and further co-operation.

In conclusion, we would emphasize the need for a non-restrictive and non-bureaucratic framework for technology imports. It is essential that all profitable enterprises have the possibility to renew their machinery and processes, by importing the technology and know-how needed (and not only the science-based industries with a clearly demonstrated potential for export).

3. Support and deregulation

All countries need an active stream of new enterprises, based on science or simply on entrepreneurship with good ideas, which are successful because they supplement the existing market supply. Development of such enterprises depends primarily on the support which they receive from surrounding environments. In this respect, we have noted an obvious commitment throughout the country to create locally such supportive environments. Very much depends on the dynamism of the responsible authorities and the degree of co-operation between the large number of socio-economic organisations. As examples of interesting initiatives that were reported to us we could mention:

– in Kosovo, at Pristina, the Regional Productivity and Innovation Centre, established since 1979, involves more than 300 collaborators from university and other organisations to provide support to innovators in technology, marketing, trade, etc. The centre undertakes studies on local development problems, inventories of products of the Province, and works of international character (e.g. for the Ljubljana Centre on Developing Countries). It initiates co-operation with counterparts abroad, e.g. in Italy, France and China. Since its creation, more than 4 000 "inventors" have been associated with the centre, notably through a network of 50 local associations established throughout the Province.

– Pula, in Croatia, has an association of inventors with a membership of about 1 500, reporting about 600 technical innovations and improvements in the recent years. Inventors are rewarded in the form of a percentage of the additional profit realised. This town intends to open a centre for innovations and technological development which would secure contributions from all interested parties. It has also obtained permission to open a "free zone" (as at Novi Sad in Vojvodina).

These are just examples among many initiatives. Success depends on the quality of leadership and staff, flexibility of the administative and financial framework, and breadth and qualification of the surrounding expert networks. As a related theme, the potential contribution of larger enterprises should be emphasized. Apart from a few cases (e.g. the shipbuilding complex Uljanik at Pula), big firms do not serve as "midwives" for new enterprises. It might be worth investigating how big industrial complexes can be motivated to assist staff members and others in establishing new firms (e.g. as sub-contractors) or to provide technical and commercial assistance to local entrepreneurs.

It is vital that an efficient patent system be established, with adequate documentation and information services. The current system does not work (e.g. 6 years for registration of patent applications without any screening!). The proposals of the Federal Committee for Science and Technology in these matters should be actively supported.

An essential element in the innovation climate is the financing system. Many sources claim that the existing economic structure is not supportive of innovation, as it is generally oriented to short-term projects rather than to risky innovative projects. In Slovenia, experience from the "Ljubljanska Banka", which supported many projects in the different phases from the idea to the finished product, shows that it is possible to develop successfully a fairly large number of export-oriented innovations when proper financing is at hand. But this successful activity seems to have been hindered by restrictive laws and a shortage of finance in recent years.

In Serbia a prerequirement for the granting of investment credits is the development of a programme for production research and innovation, including R&D activities aimed at mastering the new technologies, upgrading of work organisation, market research, etc. The interest rate is set at 50 per cent of the regular rate. As this is a new initiative, not yet approved in practice, there are no visible results. From other countries, where similar incentives exist, the overall experience is positive, especially if the credit procedure is handled in a non-bureaucratic way. It should also benefit small enterprises. At the federal level, the newly introduced tax reduction schemes for R&D and inventors seem valuable steps. Such incentives to individuals as rewards, promotion, priority in housing allocation, participation in international conferences, further education, etc. are also highly motivating.

As regards the general technical culture, the many initiatives such as "Popular Technology" – covering different associations: radio-amateurs, the Aeronautical Association, Association of Inventors, etc. are very valuable. Associations of engineers and technicians, and labour unions are also actively involved. Through exhibitions, radio and television programmes much attention has been drawn to science and technology. This must produce some positive results in the future, if the changes needed in the socio-economic system are to be realised. If not, the belief in a science-based, innovative society may end up in disillusionment and frustration.

Among the reforms to be implemented, we consider that an important issue is an increase from the present maximum of 15 of the number of employees permitted in privately owned enterprises (the authorised threshold is lower in certain Republics). We understand that these regulations are about to be reviewed. This could prove to be a useful step in encouraging both the development of new commercial enterprises and the expansion of existing small ones. As a pilot experiment, it might be feasible to permit private enterprises in a certain area to grow without fixed limits. This is one aspect of the institutional framework which appears important in the context of creating a climate for growth. Personal financial gain although important is not, of course, the only incentive for entrepreneurship. Success can be its own reward. So for example, the initiator of an enterprise which results in the creation of good jobs in an under-developed region, and which stems the flow of emigration of the best and brightest from the area, may consider himself well rewarded by the evidence of development before his eyes, and the esteem of his associates.

Other important regulations which need to be adapted relate to housing policy. At present, flats are provided by enterprises and on average it takes 10 years to acquire one. This policy, although used by some enterprises to motivate their employees, is a major barrier against mobility of people (especially professionals). Mobility is an important factor of economic dynamism in many countries. We understand that changes are also contemplated in regard to these housing regulations.

4. Time horizon: short-term actions versus changes in the system

Yugoslavia is now in a transition phase and changes are expected in forthcoming institutional arrangements as well as in the modification of the national Constitution. Such changes should attempt to establish a more market-based economy and to favour the entrepreneurial spirit of individuals and firms. The increased competitiveness of Yugoslav products would be a consequence of intended institutional changes. However, changes of the system are inherently slow in showing real effects. Excessive expectations from these changes in the system could result in delaying some actions which could start immediately.

The facts show, on the other hand, that even in the present Yugoslav system, remarkable performances are possible: consider some examples mentioned earlier such as the international success of the Institute for Earthquake Engineering in Skopje or the strong position on the ski world market achieved by ELAN. A series of short-term initiatives could improve the competitive capabilities of the country. Examples given below show some courses of action which should be seriously contemplated at this stage. These activities can be managed in the short term, do not require heavy investment and could have a considerable impact on the efficiency of industries. They relate to education and services to industry.

Yugoslav industries have to both qualify and culturally up-date their managers, by education courses in areas such as management, marketing, finance, foreign trade, technology transfer, and so on. This can be achieved through different methods: schools inside firms, education services promoted by consulting firms, independent institutes, universities, chambers of commerce, etc. The supply of education services should be flexible and adapted to the cultural and hierarchical level of users. It would be appropriate to combine education activity with research in the above mentioned areas, in co-operation with foreign institutions, where appropriate.

Management weaknesses of Yugoslav firms can also be overcome by promoting services for industry. The most urgent needs concern "soft" services, such as management consultancy, marketing, advertising, image promotion, public relations, industrial design, etc. Technical services could also be rapidly developed: software houses, engineering, feasibility studies, plant maintenance, etc. Small private organisations are, in general, the most efficient solution for such service needs, which can also be carried out or promoted by public organisations connected with chambers of commerce, manufacturers associations, local or republic authorities. Institutional flexibility is necessary, so that the entrepreneurial spirit of private individuals or of small sophisticated enterprises can be expressed freely.

The many research institutes existing throughout the territory can act as focal points of such activities. Some are already showing the way. The Institute of Field and Vegetable Crops in Novi Sad is an exemplary case of linkage between education, research and field work. The Institute is a part of the University Faculty of Agriculture. Each professor is responsible not only for teaching and research projects but also for the field work carried out in connection with teaching and research. Another feature is that the Institute is almost entirely self-financing. Income from sales of new seeds and other activities represents more than 90 per cent of its total budget. The Institute has its own stimulation incentive for innovators: when an innovation proves relevant, the innovator is awarded a participation on the income it generates throughout his working life.

5. Other critical sectors: agriculture, energy, tourism, services

The attention of the Yugoslav political world up to now has focused mainly on the solution of the problems of manufacturing industries. This is vital, but other sectors of the economy such as agriculture, services, tourism, energy conservation, environment are quite neglected. Yugoslavia too will pass from a phase of economic growth centred on manufacturing industries to a phase where conventional intersectoral barriers will fall. These barriers include the divisions between agriculture/industry/services as well as the distinction between mature and non mature sectors. All economic activities, independently of their classification, require similar management mechanisms and strategic directions; market orientation, attention to quality, selectivity in choices, strong absorption of technologies. Narrower inter-relationships between the various economic sectors lead to a revision of economic policies taking into account the fact that manufacturing industry is no longer the dominant sector but part of a wider integrated system, where primary activities (agriculture, raw materials) and services (trade, delivery, communications) exist together at the same hierarchical level alongside manufacturing industry.

Although excellent research work is already done (see above) in the agricultural sector, more efforts – such as development of excellence centres or experimental stations – are needed in view of the requirements of the country which, due to the diversity of environmental and climatic conditions, has very different patterns of agriculture between the extreme north and south as well as between the eastern and western parts. In parallel, "extension services" have to be developed for technical assistance and modernisation of farmers and co-operatives.

A further potential of Yugoslav agriculture lies in the development of non-food crops. Natural products destined for sophisticated industrial applications (cosmetics, flavours, etc.) have good market potential. This agriculture is suited also to marginal, semi-arid, montainous lands and may help significantly in providing an income for people living in underdeveloped regions. A good example is JAKA 80, a medium-sized company based in Radovis, in the Republic of Macedonia, founded in 1982 by a group of technicians who had left a big tobacco company. JAKA 80 deals mainly with production of cosmetics, pharmaceuticals and dietetic products, based on natural materials obtained from various plants, cultivated in an area of 200 hectares. In five years the company has grown from 20 to 300 employees, of whom 75 have a university or advanced degree. International agreements have been signed with western countries to supply both extracts and etheric oils, and also a complete line of finished cosmetic products.

In the most industrialised countries, the energy intensiveness of GNP (i.e. expressed as Kcal/$GNP) has been decreasing in recent decades, as economies shift towards services, efficiency and "soft" activities. As regards Yugoslavia, we were told that the energy intensity of GNP is higher than the European average and still shows an upward trend: a situation due to an economic structure largely based on heavy industries, to distortions in the prices of energy vectors (prices do not reflect costs), to the absence of incentives for energy conservation, and the absence of education on the rational use of energy sources.

Tourism development is probably the best way to yield foreign currency in the quickest time. Once again, there is a problem of quality. Yugoslavia has developed a comprehensive tourist industry, but primarily geared to attract tourists through low prices. As a result they spend around US$30 per day, while tourists in Italy spend more than US$100 daily; a problem partly due to the recruitment of tourists and partly to the difficulty of buying attractive products in Yugoslav tourist centres.

Another approach could be to develop more attractive arrangements for tourists, e.g. excursions to beautiful landscapes, historical monuments, etc., guided by some of the well educated youth who have problems in finding jobs. Hunting, fishing, sailing, etc. are activities which are well paid by wealthy tourists, who do not like to spend all their holiday at the coast. Increasing such activities has the advantage of extending the tourist season, so it is not concentrated into the short summer season. An example of high quality activities is the rehabilitation Institute "Dr. Simo Milosevic" in Igalo (Montenegro) with high standards in physical facilities as well as personal qualifications. Contracts with Norwegian and Swedish authorities demonstrate international recognition of these activities, which are closely related to the scientific work performed at the Institute and to the encouraging results obtained by the special treatments.

The immense earning potential of the tourism sector in Yugoslavia will never be realised if the "delivery system" of its goods and services, both technical and human, is not radically modernised, as was done in Sarajevo which continues its excellent development effort following the 1984 Winter Olympic Games. The delivery system's improvement includes more attention paid to quality and service standards in hotels and restaurants[9], maintenance of plumbing, lifts, etc. which in a modern State should not be allowed to deteriorate, as well as the general environment and ecology. In this matter the Yugoslav authorities seem to have taken seriously the conclusions of the recent OECD review of environment policy[10].

V. YUGOSLAVIA'S PRINCIPLES: PROBLEMS AND OPPORTUNITIES

In order to transcend its diversity and develop its unity, Yugoslavia has invented a political system based upon three main principles:
- federalism, reflecting the multinational character of the country;
- socialist self-management as the basis of the society; and
- non-alignment as the basis of an independent Yugoslav position on world affairs.

Such principles are deeply rooted in this country: any suggestions or advice aimed at improving Yugoslav science, technology, and innovation policies cannot but consider these features within which all policy proposals must be framed. The three principles of the Yugoslav system imply both advantages and disadvantages, as in any human choice. The ways in which they are interpreted and applied in practice can significantly influence the balance between positive and negative effects. We briefly examine how these principles can be positively used to increase the efficiency and competitiveness of the country.

1. Multinationality: autarky versus integration

The diversity of the Republics and Provinces constituting the Yugoslav Federation is quite marked, and there is a keen search for autonomous solutions to their problems. This diversity is, at the same time, an asset for the country and a danger.

The highly individual character of each Republic can become a negative factor when it leads to develop solutions which are as autonomous as possible. Let us repeat some examples that we mentioned earlier:

i) A consequence of the search for autonomy is the difficulty to reach a unified market at federal level, mainly for public purchases and procurements: the consequences of such market limitations are very serious for the country. The preference in federal units for purchasing locally produced goods, independently of their competitiveness from both price and performance points of view, is a further straining factor which limits the possibilities of improving the technological quality of products.

ii) The lack of a unified system of metrology and technical standards also contributes to these problems. In key areas such as telecommunications, new standards have been established without co-ordination between Republics.

iii) The absence of federal institutes of advanced technologies favours the duplication, in the various Republics, of similar initiatives below the critical efficiency thresholds.

The way of separate development and self-sufficiency seems to be a constraint for the future of the Republics. On the other hand, autonomy has to be maintained as a strong tie with the republics' historical and economical vocations, traditions, natural, cultural and artistic resources. When properly oriented and exploited, a large variety of cultures and natural environments can become a critical success factor. The tie with the territorial vocations is then a very important element of competitive strength. Many Yugoslav activities which have proved to be successful at an international level are strongly rooted in the territory and in local vocations, as illustrated by practically all the examples provided throughout this report.

Each Republic has to endeavour to identify its own role within the wider federal system. The development of economic activities in the individual Republics, once a minimum basic level is reached, should not aim to cover the whole productive spectrum, but should exploit and further develop individual strong points: revitalising and strengthening conventional industries, craftsmanship, agriculture and tourism are often more efficient ways than the creation of industrial poles centred on basic industries alien to the surrounding environment ("cathedrals in the desert"). Renewal and modernisation of traditional activities involve great advantages as compared to industrialisation in heavy manufacturing sectors: low capital-intensiveness, provision of more qualified jobs, strong absorption of new technologies, creation of advanced marketing and financing systems, etc.

Policies implemented in less favoured regions in the past have not had the intended effect: e.g. the practice of giving soft loans to attract investors to less developed regions has not stimulated the selection of profitable new enterprises and other projects. On the contrary, in a number of cases, the establishment of large and expensive plants has created new problems, due to the fact that general economic and profitability principles were not sufficiently considered before making such investments.

The highest research potential – and educational activities – exist naturally in the most developed regions in the northern part of the country and in Serbia. The challenge is to create structures and programmes furthering a constructive collaboration between North and South in research as well as in practical co-operation between enterprises, instead of reinforcing regional barriers or developing independent research units isolated from national and international efforts and policies.

An essential positive factor is that the education of young people in the 1980s is nearly equal in all regions, and quantitatively at a sufficient level as regards the proportion of young people entering universities and similar higher level education. Naturally, differences in the quality of education in the different regions do emerge; opinions differ as to whether these differences are increasing or decreasing.

It must be realised, however, that a federal structure with limited power and capacity for co-ordination constitutes, *de facto*, a limitation on efforts to establish a more evenly developed nation.

2. Self-management: from confrontation to responsibility

In order to ensure the necessary dynamism and creativeness in modern economies, it is essential that appropriate conditions exist for the participation of individuals and groups in the life of firms and other organisations. From this point of view, Yugoslavia's self management approch deserves special comment. The philosophy of workers' self-management means that all workers have the right to participate in decisions affecting every level of the organisation of the enterprise, i.e. what is produced, methods of production, marketing, R&D, hours of work and wages, the dispersal of profits or management of a loss.

This system has both potential strengths and weaknesses. The strengths relate mainly to the fuller involvement, and hence the potential for greater commitment of workers to their enterprise. The weaknesses relate to a pyramid system of decision making, which involves many layers of consultation, reporting and balloting, which inevitably both slows down the decision-making process, and rules out innovative initiatives unless all the basic organisations of associated labour (BOAL) within an enterprise agree to their adoption.

The presence of BOAL in the working organisations (i.e. the enterprises) is a central feature in the Yugoslav system (it should be pointed out that there are also working organisations operating without BOAL). An efficient contribution of BOAL to the management of firms requires a cultural level and a civic sense which probably are lacking in all countries, not only in Yugoslavia. The self-management system in practice does appear as an element of disturbance and politicisation in the management of firms. This is proved to be true by the fact that most of the successful firms that we visited either do not consider BOAL as relevant or have decided to abolish them. The same trends are observable in research institutes.

It seems then desirable to reduce the powers of BOAL when they are antagonistic to the management of firms. However, BOAL will probably remain to some extent a distinctive feature of the Yugoslav economy: it would be therefore wise to search for ways to render such basic organisations more efficient and more oriented towards contributions to the growth of the firm. In other words, it is necessary to find solutions giving to BOAL a larger concern for the success of their working organisations.

Appropriate mechanisms relate to the correlation between salaries and productivity, the creation of quality circles, increased utilisation and widening of the Register of Innovators and so on. The problem of the lack of motivation for innovation cannot, indeed, be solved only by the offer of economic incentives: stimulating factors are the success of the firm itself, the self-realisation of workers, the power deriving from success. In the success stories examined, the higher salaries of employees were not the cause of the entrepreneurial spirit, but rather an effect of it.

In a nutshell, self-management has been so far conceived as a tool to control the distributive side of the economy; more attention needs to be given to the creative side on which depends the generation of wealth to be shared. A priori, such a bottom-up system should be receptive to the institutional innovations mentioned above. However three conditions need to be fulfilled:

i) The status of knowledge needs to be broadened: the view reducing knowledge to science leads to neglect of the basic worker as a producer of knowledge, a feature which appears completely contradictory with sound self-management principles. A proof of this non-recognition of the basic worker in his/her creative dimension lies in the clear separation which is made between the "producers" of knowledge (i.e. the "scientists") and the "users" of knowledge (i.e. the others), joining together in the so called "Self-management Communities of Interest for Science". This distinction between "producers" and "users" of knowledge is rather questionable. The recognition of the basic worker as a producer of knowledge is fundamental if there is any chance of seeing the development of quality circles and so on in the economy. A worker in a factory, a peasant in a field, a waiter in an hotel are all engaged in a kind of research (generating-knowledge) process, as soon as they try to improve the quality of their products or services. Their potential contribution to the country's well being, or to its trade balance, are as essential as the potential contribution of the scientists.

ii) A second condition is to think "small". The importance of small units (small enterprises, small groups, etc.) in the development of OECD countries is obvious, not because "small is beautiful" but because it fits with the current technological evolution (e.g. information technology) and is better for mastering it (e.g. flexibility). In Yugoslavia's industry, it seems that most of the BOAL are relatively big (often more than 100 people), and it is difficult to see new smaller ones appearing spontaneously.

iii) A third condition necessary for improvement of the self-management system is that it be submitted to more "competition" from any other possible forms of organisation: small private businesses, co-operatives, contractual organisations[11], etc. If the possibilities of economic development using other forms are not increased, pressure for improvement in the self management organisation will be insufficient.

When applying these three conditions, great flexibility could be maintained within the whole territory, as each Federal Unit has a different background. For instance, we have noted that in certain parts of Yugoslavia big industrial enterprises tend to be more centralised than in other parts but that does not prevent the development of competitive enterprises in advanced technology in both cases. In other places, where there is a strong tradition of business and commerce, people get by easily with any form of organisation: socialistic, private, "hybrid", etc. which all seem, in fact, to be managed in a rather pragmatic way.

3. Non-Alignment: island or bridge

Yugoslavia has traditionally assumed a leadership position in the international movement of Non-Aligned Countries. This position has been considered as ambiguous by the Eastern Bloc as well as by the Western Bloc. Although the country has agreements with European economic organisations such as EEC, EFTA and COMECON, it lacks the opportunities to participate in the wider continental markets and it finds difficulties in being involved in large technological development projects, such as, for example, EUREKA.

The present choice designed to introduce "more market into the country" would facilitate the development of closer relations with Western Europe. However, in the view of the Examiners, it is difficult to see how full integration with the EEC could be achieved at the present time considering the important differences between the Yugoslav economic and political system and the ones in place in Western Europe.

Paralleling a policy of approaching the Western World, it would be worthwhile to consider opportunities arising from assuming a leading role in collaboration with developing countries. Efforts in this direction could be encouraged, such as the launching of large development projects, realisation of international research centres and major training and education programmes for students of the Third World.

As a by-product of its non-aligned position, and of some disappointing and costly experiences with foreign technology, there is, as we have seen, a certain tendency to think that Yugoslavia should generate much more of its own technology. However, in the view of the Examiners, smaller countries like Yugoslavia must accept that more than 90 per cent of the new technology they use is developed outside the country. In building an appropriate capacity for absorption, Yugoslavia can become a kind of "technology bridge" between the North and the South. Some initiatives quoted above pave the way. As a first step it would be appropriate to concentrate on the Mediterranean area, where Yugoslavia could play a more important role.

To a certain extent, with its own internal tensions both East-West and North-South, Yugoslavia is a sort of world in miniature. Reducing these tensions requires pragmatism and acceptance of pluralism. Being a mirror of the world confers some responsibility. It may be also considered as a positive element, as the country could become a kind of laboratory for development of experience of broader interest than only to itself.

VI. SUGGESTED POLICY ACTIONS

As the President of the Federal Committee for Science and Technology stated when we met him during the review visit "there are hard times to come". But the country is aware of the gravity of the problems, has the cultural and material capabilities to meet the challenge, and has identified appropriate paths to follow. The cohesion of the nation as a whole and the sense of responsibility of all citizens will be critical to success, and will also be necessary to overcome dogmatic views and conservative behaviour, protecting established positions.

In view of the particular organisation of Yugoslav society and the very diffuse exercise of power which characterises it, we have formulated policy orientations of general interest, to be considered by everybody concerned, at all levels of society. These orientations summarise the suggestions provided throughout the report. They should be seen also as supporting the steps already taken, or progressive intentions expressed in Yugoslavia, as described in the draft Background Report.

These policy orientations will be grouped under four headings: the building up of a knowledge-intensive society, the improvement of the technological performance of the economy, the adaptation of the socio-institutional framework, and the further internationalisation of Yugoslavia's economy, science and technology. These lines need to be pursued together, within a systems view[12]. However, before detailing them we feel it necessary to comment on the need for concrete action.

Ambitions are great, analyses are right, strategies are clear, but the translation to efficient, simple action is achieved only with extreme difficulty in Yugoslavia. The importance given to "discourse" over action is considerable. This is illustrated, among other things, by the time devoted to talks and plans before making any decision (and the belief that the action will necessarily follow), the belief in, and waiting for, system changes. Moreover, when innovative initiatives are taken, they are often hindered by bureaucratic obstacles or regulatory attitudes. These should be eliminated.

1. Building up a knowledge-intensive society

i) Supporting actions of the Federal Committee for Science and Technology

We believe that the Draft Strategy of Technological Development of Yugoslavia prepared by the Committee should be supported and sufficient resources allocated, i.e. around US$100 million, to the Federal Fund established to stimulate technological development of industry. Conditions of allocations of federal aid should avoid any form of bureaucratisation and redistributive criteria. The establishment, or improvement, of federal mechanisms for patent protection, standardisation, metrology, scientific and technical information and R&D statistics should receive high priority and be actively supported. It is also advisable that measures concerning the scientific and technological policy adopted at federal level be integrated with other policies aimed at establishing a more innovative climate, such as:

housing policy, taxation policy, small business promotion, government purchases, mobility policy, etc.

ii) Increasing and focus the research effort

The proportion of Yugoslav GDP allocated to R&D activities must be increased in the future; the growth rate should depend more on the quality of proposals and anticipated effects on economic and social development, than on quantitative figures concerning number of researchers, or percentages arbitrarily fixed in advance. The best R&D projects, especially in fundamental and applied research, should be supported through federal funds, which should aim at national and international integration of research projects and at creation of national centres of excellence. The improvement of a national network of high quality R&D institutions should be given a high priority. With a view to establishing internationally-oriented centres of excellence, which can act as nuclei for basic research, priority should be given to R&D institutions which have already demonstrated talent and have achieved good results and have the capacity to present plans and projects of high interest for the society as a whole. There is also a need to be selective in the choice of priority research areas to be funded by the Fund mentioned above. Particular attention should be given to technologies which are related to areas of natural advantage (e.g. agriculture and tourism) and to industrial fields with demonstrated technological competitiveness. Moreover at all levels, and notably in the Self-Management Communities of Interest for Science, current practices for the funding of R&D should be reviewed with the aim of providing more support to long-term or far-sighted projects and to development of new domestic technologies and products.

iii) Intensifying the education effort

Improved mechanisms to upgrade skills are needed at all levels, manual workers as well as managers, teachers and scientists. This requires a multi-targeted effort including adjustments to curricula, modernisation of teaching materials, methods and equipment (computers, videos), etc. Managers, scientists, and talented youth should receive high priority in obtaining grants to study abroad. The upgrading of competences in industry would benefit from immediate mobilisation of education and research institutions with support of regional and local organisations such as chambers of commerce. Collaboration between Self-Management Communities of Interest for Science and Self-Management Communities of Interest for Education would help in forecasting and planning training needs, notably as regards engineers. As the future development of the country depends, to a high degree, on the society's interest in science, technology and innovation, it is vital to attract talented youth to the most appropriate educational areas. Initiatives should be taken not only by schools and universities, but also by industry, radio and television. A reliable vision of Yugoslavia as a nation based on a talented use of science and technology for developing human welfare should be presented through the different media. Selected cases of successful scientists, inventors and entrepreneurs would be presented, so that heroes for the nation would not be exclusively great football players and rock musicians.

2. Improving the country's technological performance

i) Strengthening technological capability in industry

Most of industrial research and development work should be carried out as close to the market as possible, in industrial enterprises. These should be supported by research institutes and consultants. The R&D potential of industry should be improved through recruitment of good young researchers, tax incentives and low interest loans. Enterprises with demonstrated success, or great potential, in export and efficient research groups should benefit from priority in access to foreign currency for investment in new technology and know-how, purchase of scientific instruments and participation in international events, etc. Public organisations (e.g. in health care, transportation, etc.) should use their potential as large buyers of technology to support development of new competitive products, e.g. through development contracts, and should reduce bureaucratic practices and restrictive attitudes.

ii) Increasing productivity and quality in the economy

Productivity, quality control, energy consumption and general attitudes to maintenance are critical factors in Yugoslav industry in particular, and society in general. These factors are not primarily related to scientific research, but it is absolutely necessary to improve the situation radically in these areas. This might be done without spending much foreign currency, but by learning from the most efficient firms and organisations. Good management practices need to be much more broadly diffused, with more attention given to competence, responsibility and incentives, as well as to sanctions for those employees and managers who do not fulfil appropriate requirements of work efficiency. Moreover a national quality-control campaign in industry should be established; key research institutes in each Republic should be given the responsibility to lead this campaign.

iii) Extending support and services to innovators

Local and regional organisations (e.g. innovation centres) established for helping inventors, innovators and entrepreneurs should be encouraged and receive appropriate human and financial resources. These organisations should also provide funding for innovative projects (prototype, product development, market studies, etc.), in using approaches which have proved to be efficient in Yugoslavia and abroad. Consultancy services for management, marketing, technology, design, software, etc. need to be enlarged by systematically building networks with existing expertise in local education and research institutes and by facilitating development of specialised small businesses. Large industrial organisations should examine ways to assist in creating new small enterprises which might serve as sub-contractors or start production in new fields.

3. Adapting the socio-institutional framework

i) Deepening the concept of self-management

The creative dimension of self-management as a general organisation principle of the Yugoslav society needs to be further developed. This may take, for instance, the form of the establishment of quality circles, making better use of the Registers of Innovators and so on. Key factors lie not only in economic incentives but also in the delegation of responsibility to smaller groups (within the "basic organisation of associated labour") and recognition of creativeness at the shopfloor. On the other hand, delegation of responsibility upward could streamline vital decision-making and management in enterprises which, as an executive function, cannot be the responsibility of the workers' councils. It should be of general interest to conduct a systematic study of the variations in operation of the self-management system, with a view to isolating the factors most contributory to success, in the more efficient institutes and enterprises, and, on the other hand, identifying the most prevalent obstacles in the less successful cases. Successful examples should be widely publicised throughout the whole country.

ii) Developing a more market-led economy

The practice of allowing loss-making industries to continue to operate without any radical changes must be reduced and a market-based approach introduced as quickly as possible; this would include plans for the rehabilitation of industries considered as potentially profitable after restructuring. Openness of local markets to suppliers of other Republics or Provinces should be increased; the practice of republican or provincial organisations purchasing locally produced goods, independently of their competitiveness, should be abandoned. Joint approaches between Republics would be adopted as regards fixation of technical and commercial standards, at least in a series of basic technologies such as telecommunication equipment. Restrictions against the establishment and growth of new enterprises should be reduced, e.g. limits concerning the number of employees in private enterprises should be softened to motivate entrepreneurs to start and enlarge competitive enterprises. More generally, administratrive controls over prices, foreign currencies, investments, etc. should be reduced. Such controls distort the economic reality, hamper initiatives and justify inertia, instead of stimulating necessary efforts for productivity, quality, technology and other qualitative factors.

iii) Improving programmes in favour of less developed regions

The development of less favoured regions should be based more on traditional industries, craftmanship, agriculture and tourism. These should be given priority over industrialisation in heavy sectors. Systematic inventories of business opportunities and needs should be undertaken, and followed up with appropriate action: technical assistance, product promotion, export support, etc. Establishment of joint ventures with firms of the more advanced regions would be mutually beneficial. Actions should be focused on the creation of quality jobs for the local population with attractive effects. Large investments are required to provide technical and managerial training (and retraining) facilities through joint efforts with institutions of the most advanced regions.

4. Internationalising Yugoslav science and technology

i) Improving conditions of absorption of foreign technology

Co-operation with foreign industry should be encouraged, particularly when such arrangements include imports of technology unknown in Yugoslavia and considered as essential for future development. Arrangements should include few or no restrictions on Yugoslav (re)export and should give the Yugoslav and foreign partners an equal status in co-operation. In parallel, the Yugoslav enterprises' capabilities in technology transfer and licensing negociation should be improved by appropriate efforts within enterprises and the establishment of training programmes in universities and similar schools; consideration should also be given to establishment of a Federal Advisory Council which would assemble existing expertise and experience in industry. The planned Free Trade Areas constitute an interesting instrument for attracting science-based and export-oriented industries, rather than simple assembly factories and low-cost productions.

ii)   Enlarging international co-operation

Opportunities arising from international co-operation need to be increased by mutual efforts on the part of both Yugoslavia and foreign countries. As regards scientific co-operation, it is absolutely essential that the Yugoslav authorities ensure appropriate working conditions for those research teams initiating co-operation programmes with foreign partners, as well as maximise benefit of such international co-operation, e.g. in focusing on development of excellence centres of national interest. As regards co-operation of a more technological and industrial character, it would be appropriate to explore further the opportunities offered by transnational programmes, notably at EEC level. In parallel, co-operation efforts with the developing countries should be intensified, notably in the Mediterranean area. As regards the development of scientific co-operation and technology transfer, notably with the most advanced countries, it is recommended that better use be made of Yugoslav scientists and technologists who have emigrated abroad and constitute potential networks that could be motivated and quickly activated.

iii)   Developing selected short-term actions

In a short term perspective, a number of fine-tuned and well-calibrated actions could usefully contribute to create a better climate for progress and innovation in specific areas. To support Yugoslav efforts in scientific information, OECD countries could facilitate increased co-operation through access to data bases, and could provide Yugoslavia with information in research activities in priority fields (e.g. name and institute of researcher with title of research project), etc. A further consideration in this field could be the short term secondment of a small team of Yugoslav experts to study the systems of assessment and evaluation of R&D projects and major research funding bodies abroad. In a similar vein, it would be appropriate to select a corps of talented people to be sent, e.g. for one year, to advanced business schools abroad; these people would then provide further teaching in Yugoslav institutions. Finally it is recommended to attract foreign experts, who can be helpful in alerting all sectors (industry, agriculture, services) to the importance of design, quality, maintenance and productivity improvements. With the help of such experts, an awareness programme on a national scale could be developed, based on selected (successful) cases and using modern media (video, TV, etc.). The OECD Co-operative Action Programme with Yugoslavia could usefully contribute to initiate and establish such training oriented projects.

*
*   *

All these directions will need to be maintained for a number of years, as points to be headed for by the "pilot of the boat" whatever the events. It would be essential to review systematically, year after year, progress accomplished along all these lines. That may also help in understanding what are the factors of change and resistance, as well as how the whole society is moving towards *action.*

NOTES AND REFERENCES

1. The importance of recognising the unique nature of countries under review was stressed at the workshop held at OECD in June 1986, at the initiative of Yugoslavia, for studying the methods and impacts of these reviews. Thus a review should introduce to a kind of "ethno-analysis" through which the country concerned can become more aware of its ethos, with its strengths and weaknesses. See: "Reviews of science and technology policies and innovation policies in OECD Member countries – methodologies and impacts". Document in general distribution (109 pp.).

2. *OECD Economic Surveys – Yugoslavia*, Paris, January 1987.

3. See *Science in a Peripheral Country*, Professor Ivo Slaus, ESF Communications nº 16, European Science Foundation, Strasbourg, February 1987.

4. *Science Policy Review – Yugoslavia*, OECD, Paris, 1975.

5. This principle of organisation is applied throughout the whole society from basic organisational units to functional or municipal communities and finally to republican and provincial assemblies. At this level, they constitute the so-called fourth chamber of the assemblies and they take part in the enactment of laws, resolutions and outlines of research strategies. The "service users" component of the assembly is supposed to represent the entire social spectrum and thus to ensure an appropriate democratisation of the science and technology policy. For more detail, see *Science in Yugoslavia*, Zagreb, 1980 (prepared in connection with the 21st General Conference of UNESCO, Belgrade, September-October 1980).

6. Federal support would amount to a different percentage depending on the project initiator: 30 per cent of project cost when initiated by enterprises, 40 per cent when it is by a foreign organisation, 10 per cent when it is by a SCIS, and 30 per cent when it comes from the army.

7. *Reviews of National Policies for Education – Yugoslavia*, OECD, Paris, 1981.

8. The beginnings of ELAN go back to a "partisan" ski workshop which in 1944-45 supplied military forces of Slovenian mountains with skis. By the end of the fifties, after a disappointing diversification in badminton rackets, the firm developed a very agressive policy to expand its production and export of skis. This included notably the establishment of a research centre (the first industrial R&D institute in Slovenia, founded in 1963), and a systematic approach of new markets such as those in Scandinavian. In doing this, ELAN found exceptional Alpine racers, such as I. Stenmark (Sweden), who promoted its image. Now ELAN is the second producer of alpine skis in the world. It has been sponsoring a number of world ski competitions. Apart from skis, ELAN is involved in gymnastics equipment, pleasure crafts and gliders. To produce the gliders, ELAN bought initially a German licence and attracted hobbyists to build them, thus ensuring excellent quality-control, testing, and marketing. ELAN has received a number of national and international awards for creativity, quality and productivity. It could constitute an enlightening case study for business and design schools throughout the world.

9. As in manufacturing, much progress can be achieved by simple, not expensive, steps. It does not cost much more to serve the morning coffee hot than serving it cold, or to provide a "do not disturb" sign to guests, or to employ a friendly and competent switchboard operator. A growing number of Yugoslav hotels have realised those simple things (notably when associated with foreign hotel

chains), so enhancing the extraordinary, natural hospitality of Yugoslav people. They provide examples that should be emulated.

10. *Environment policies in Yugoslavia*, OECD, Paris, 1986.

11. Contractual firms are based on a particular mechanism through which the founder, as a private entrepreneur, is paid back for his initial capital investment through a ten year period. He can then decide to reinvest this capital in the firm; in case he does not, the enterprise becomes socially-owned. However, these "hybrid" companies, introduced some years ago, do not seem very attractive, since there are only one or two hundred such firms throughout the country.

12. The need for such a systemic approach when all problems have to be tackled together at the same time was notably emphasized by the workshop "Innovation policy in less industrialised OECD countries", held at Dubrovnik in September 1983 (see the report in general distribution).

Part III

ACCOUNT OF THE REVIEW MEETING

I. INTRODUCTION

The meeting was held at Dubrovnik, on 25th October 1987.

It was opened by *Mr. Branko Mikulic*, President of the Federal Executive Council of the Federal Socialist Republic of Yugoslavia. In his address (see Preface), Mr. Mikulic stressed the importance of the review, which justified the commitment of Yugoslavia to a science and technology based development. The Federal Science and Technology Strategy was the first to be adopted in a series of strategies aimed at restoring Yugoslavia's economy. Accepting the rules of a market economy should stimulate further adjustment of Yugoslav enterprises. Market forces would help in using the synergistic qualities of socialist self management. Mr. Mikulic re-affirmed the position of Yugoslavia as a non-aligned, European, Mediterranean country, which is not an isolated island but has a key role in developing human, cultural and peace aspects, notably as regards the Third World. Mr. Mikulic expressed the satisfaction of the Yugoslav Government regarding the reports prepared for the review.

Mr. Jones, Minister for Science and Small Business, Australia, Chairman of the meeting expressed, on behalf of OECD, warm thanks to Mr. Mikulic for his presence. He underlined the symbolic significance of the choice of Dubrovnik, as place for the meeting, in view of the historical tradition of quality, independance and dynamism manifested by the city. He noted that neither the Background Report nor the Examiners' Report had avoided issues fundamental to the Yugoslav society, and he expressed the wish that these issues be further discussed at the meeting which, he said, should not be a "festival of blandness".

The head of the Yugoslav Delegation, *Mr. Matic*, President of the Federal Committee for Science and Technology, expressed the thanks of the Yugoslav authorities to the OECD, the Examiners and the Secretariat for the competence and enthusiasm with which this review had been conducted and the reports prepared. At a time of a major technological revolution and an intensive restructuring of Yugoslav economy there was a need for a good diagnosis, more objective than if done by the Yugoslav themselves. This explained why this OECD review was so highly valued.

Mr. Marcum, OECD Director for Science, Technology and Industry, underlined the quality of the intellectual and organisational support provided by the Yugoslav authorities throughout the whole process of the review. He stressed that technical change was now well recognised as a key factor in economic growth and social development, as illustrated by the Nobel Prize in Economics which had recently been awarded to Professor Robert Solow of Massachussetts Institute of Technology for his revolutionary work in this field. Mr. Marcum noted the large participation of other OECD countries to the meeting – a source of strength for Yugoslavia in facing its current problems – and expressed the appreciation of OECD for the attendance of the Prime Minister, which was an indication of the determination of Yugoslavia to move ahead in solving very critical problems.

The Chairman of the meeting invited then the participants to discuss the Examiners' Report.

II. THE SCIENCE AND TECHNOLOGY SYSTEM AND THE CLIMATE FOR INNOVATION

Mrs. Aylward introduced the discussion on the scientific and technological system, by focusing on some major weaknesses which were preventing an efficient exploitation of the Yugoslav research potential. Firstly, the spirit of independance and the rivalry which characterised the Federal Units led to fragmentation and duplication of effort, most of the projects being under the necessary critical mass; in this respect the OECD report welcomed the Federal Strategy and the Federal Fund for Technological Development. Secondly, a large amount of applied research done on behalf of industry was not led by market efficiency criteria, because of the particular conditions in which Yugoslav enterprises were operating. Thirdly, research efforts throughout the country were not sufficiently focused on strengths and comparative advantages. Tourism was an area of comparative advantage, and excellent results could be obtained, as illustrated by the magnificent effort of Sarajevo for the 1984 Olympic Games.

Mrs. Aylward suggested, as a metaphor, that winning in technological competition is like wining in a sports race. She mentioned the example of the Tour de France, the bicycle race won this year by an Irishman who might have not been intrinsically the strongest, but who was selective in his efforts, and supported by an excellent team of people working together. She indicated that Ireland, although smaller and more centralised than Yugoslavia, had also met problems of regional fragmentation of research effort. A solution had been found in having a national strategy which was not centrally led. For instance, a western region of Ireland was given responsibility for co-ordinating marine research, and a southern region was asked to co-ordinate efforts in electronics. After receiving proposals from six universities for the creation of research centres in biotechnology, the Government decided to select only three – each focused on small research niches where Ireland had competence and needs.

Mr. Knudsen underlined the quality of the Background Report prepared by the Yugoslav authorities, whose analyses were entirely approved by the review team, but he noted that the major problem of Yugoslavia was to get things moving. Introducing the discussion on the climate for innovation and growth, he stressed that basic research could in no way help in solving the most acute problems of Yugoslavia, although it might have a longer-term significance and was also essential to maintain good intellectual and scientific relations at international level with advanced countries. The most immediate problems to be solved in Yugoslavia related to the situation of industry. Productivity needed to be improved. The right to go bankrupt, as a factor of dynamism, was important. The management of enterprises was very weak: this was largely due to the painful decision-making process which characterised the Yugoslav enterprises. There should be a clear right to fire as well to hire people. Raising the quality of products should be a major objective, particularly through the widespread development of quality circles, taking advantage of the self-management approach, getting inspiration from the Japanese experience and changing the present "low price" mentality.

Mr. Knudsen drew attention to other critical factors mentioned in the Examiners' Report: the need for improved collaboration between enterprises and authorities in relation to public procurement, the need for developing enterprises' capabilities in negotiating and absorbing technology imports, the need to avoid focusing on industry but also to exploit advantages in agriculture, tourism and so on. As an example of a high quality activity in tourism, he mentioned the Institute of Rehabilitation in Igalo, Montenegro, that he had visited during the review mission. Mr. Knudsen considered this to be a good example of the change needed to leave behind outmoded attitudes and to enter a new innovative era. Such a change would be applied to every aspect of the life.

In a brief response to comments made by the Examiners, *Mr. Matic* stressed that, since the review visit in April, a number of actions had been taken showing the willingness of Yugoslavia to revise its economic system. Bankruptcy reforms had been implemented, and a number of enterprises had gone bankrupt as result of new laws. People who had lost their job through this process had been assisted while seeking new jobs. The accounting system had been adapted to force enterprises to show real economic performance. Mr. Matic thought also that the Examiners might have misunderstood some aspects of the self-management system, which was most efficient as regards workers' participation and did not constitute obstacles to innovation.

Mr. Matejic, Delegate of Yugoslavia to the CSTP, noted that the Yugoslav Delegation was in agreement with the Examiners' major criticism of the research system. The lack of co-ordination and insufficient development of R&D potential in industry were two serious problems. In a transitory phase, particular attention would be paid to the independant institutes which accounted for 60 per cent of the research potential of the country. Mr. Matejic thought that the Examiners might have underestimated market forces already at work in the Yugoslav economy, which are to be strengthened by recent policy changes. These changes would invisibly contribute to co-ordinating research efforts. In relation to concerns expressed by Examiners on declining university enrolments in scientific and engineering studies, Mr. Matejic indicated a positive trend among youngsters who were now increasingly interested in such studies. However, they would have a hard time finding a job in Yugoslavia and there would be some "brain drain". This issue should be put in a broader international perspective, with appropriate co-operation programmes.

Mr. Vratusa, Member of the Council of the Federation, noted that the OECD report would probably become a reference book. In this respect, while the report has penetrated the essence of the Yugoslav society, it would be necessary to pay particular attention in the final version to some words or judgments which might not be accurate or could lead to misinterpretations. As an example, he mentioned the Examiners' comments on decentralis-ation. Decentralisation has been an essential instrument of democratisation; problems have come from the absence of appropriate mechanisms for co-ordination. More generally he felt that most of the problems were related to the implementation of the self-management system rather than to the principles of the system, which were sound.

Mr. Varadi, President of the Association of Self Management Communities of Interest for Science of Yugoslavia, agreed that fragmentation of the research system was a serious problem. Efforts to overcome this had been made at the level of the communities for science, which recently had to decide on 14 federal projects. The OECD report was an encouragement to their efforts. As regards Mr. Knudsen's comments, Mr. Varadi mentioned that there had, in fact, been a law for 25 years allowing bankruptcy, but that there had been no mechanism to get rid of those economic units which were not viable. As regards another issue identified by Examiners, namely the lack of a unified market between Republics, the constitution provided rules for unification, but there were no penalties for those who infringed such rules. As a third example, he noted that the self-management rules did not imply that workers' councils should be involved in the day-to-day management of enterprises. There is a clear distinction between the so-called "inalienable rights" of workers, and management as an executive function. Here again it was more the implementation of the system than its principles which were causing trouble.

Mr. Srica, President of the Committee for Science, Technology and Computer Science of Croatia, had some difficulty with the notion of comparative advantage and the advice to focus on natural advantages of Yugoslavia, such as agriculture, forestry and tourism. He stated that the advanced countries had often created areas of comparative advantages rather than inheriting them. This was particularly the case for high technology areas, and Mr. Scrica wanted to know the opinion of the Examiners as regards Yugoslavia. As a related issue, he questioned the re-export policy advocated by the Examiners, who had singled out the success of the enterprise Nicholas Tesla. Such a re-export policy had proved in the past to be highly costly and had created balance of payments problems. More generally, this put in question the image of a "technology bridge" proposed for Yugoslavia by the Examiners.

In response to comments and questions by the Yugoslav Delegation, *Mr. Knudsen* stressed several points. Firstly, as regards bankruptcy and related unemployment, there was a need for extensive re-education in promising fields. That was costly but efficient, as illustrated for instance in Denmark with women without qualifications who have been trained in electronics, through intensive courses. There was also a need to develop responsibility and elitism in the self-management system, as in basic research and in sport. As regards decentralisation which is a good thing, co-ordination can be improved by big strategic programmes at federal level. This approach had been successful in Denmark. In this respect, Mr. Knudsen repeated that the establishment of the Federal Fund and Strategy was a critical step in the right direction. He stressed also the need for global vision, noting that some Republics like Serbia have attempted to elaborate such goals, but no similar effort had been made for Yugoslavia as a whole. To build up such a goal or vision, the particular position of Yugoslavia as regards both East-West and North-South relationships needed to be further exploited. This would constitute a natural advantage on which concrete strategies could be developed.

Mrs. Aylward confirmed that the problem was a question of co-ordination and not of decentralisation. But the more a system is decentralised, the more it needs to be well co-ordinated. As regards the issue of natural advantages, it was not the intention of the Examiners to focus on things like Yugoslavia's nice climate and beautiful landscape, but to draw attention to the need to relate the technological effort to Yugoslavia's advantages and opportunities. This required a difficult assessment of capacities existing in industry, in higher education, etc.

As regards comparative advantages, *Professor Galli* emphasized the need to have a comprehensive view of technical change. Advanced technologies should not be developed for their own sake, but have a critical role in fertilizing traditional activities in industry, agriculture and services. Thus policies should not be focused only on R&D, but also on the diffusion of new technologies, including factors such as education, regulation, etc. which determine the conditions of diffusion. In Italy, the enterprises which are the most effective in absorbing advanced technologies and methods (marketing, organisation) are those operating in traditional sectors (e.g. textiles, agriculture), not those operating in the so-called "high tech" sectors (e.g. telecommunications).

Mr. Aubert agreed that self management was very complex and that the review team might not have fully understood some of its aspects. However there was one thing on which the review team was sure: so far the creative side of self management had not been sufficiently developed. Self management has been generally seen as a system to redistribute wealth. The opportunities offered for generating such wealth have not been explored. In any event, developing creative self management was fundamental for the survival of the Yugoslav society.

Following comments on the Japanese experience, *Professor Inose*, Chairman of the CSTP, reminded participants that a workshop on innovation policy in less industrialised OECD countries had been held in Dubrovnik four years earlier, in September 1983, and that two papers from Japan had been distributed to the participants. One paper, prepared by a researcher from United Nations University in Tokyo, explained the strategic path followed by Japan to build a "high technology" nation starting from a predominantly agricultural base. The other paper described the establishment of a quality circle in an automobile factory and was written by the foreman responsible for this circle. Professor Inose thought that it would be worthwhile to look again at these two papers.

Following the example of Japan, however, raised some questions. There were two basic attitudes when competing in the world market. The first could be expressed as: "everything you can do, I can do it better"; the second could be "something you cannot do, I can do". A number of countries tended to adopt the first attitude. For instance the new industrialised countries in Asia were "looking East" towards Japan and copying it. There was a need for other countries to look at the Japanese experience with critical eyes, and to seek for market niches. Denmark, for example, exports to Japan a large volume of hearing aids based on a very sophisticated technology. This is typical of the approach of the small advanced countries, such as the Nordic countries. Yugoslavia has a scientific tradition as illustrated by Nicholas Tesla who influenced the progress of world science. This tradition needs to be encouraged. The development of centres of excellence might help in restoring a sense of high quality, while helping general co-ordination. Yugoslav universities also need to reconsider and reorganise their whole curricula in order to inject a spirit of competition, excellence and quality.

Professor Landberg, Delegate from Sweden, was impressed by the open, frank and broad perspective offered both by the Examiners' Report and the Background Report. The latter was an excellent starting point for further analysis and change. He emphasized the need for a system approach, as shown by the reports: the accumulation of problems in many varied parts of the whole system had made it inefficient. Here the creative side of self management has not be developed because there was, for instance, no appropriate delegation of responsibility or motivation of teams of workers. The problems of lack of co-ordination of the research effort arose from the particular way it was financed and from the regional autonomy, etc. The accumulation of tensions in many parts of the system made the risk of disintegration very high. In the view of Professor Landberg, science and technology itself could be a very useful tool for achieving a higher degree of national integration in Yugoslavia, a vital aspect for the future.

In the view of *Mrs. Krawczynski*, Delegate of Germany, Yugoslavia was very courageous in asking OECD to undertake this review, which is a rather critical process. She considered that several points made by the OECD report touched some deep socio-cultural and psychological aspects. For instance, making progress on co-ordination required overcoming long-standing feudal behaviour. This was a challenge for politicians, who should aim at recreating a sense of the federation and unity for the whole nation.

Mr. Green, Delegate of Australia, suggested that Yugoslavia could usefully examine mechanisms which had worked in other countries to develop R&D in industry, although the Yugoslav economy had very specific features. In Australia, good results have been obtained through tax incentives. A programme has been in place for three years allowing enterprises to write off up to 150 per cent their R&D expenditures. As a result, industry's share of total R&D in Australia has increased from 20 per cent to 40 per cent. Public research organisations, like the Commonwealth Scientific Industrial Research Organisation, have also been forced to work more closely with industry on a contractual basis.

Mr. Vribalovitch, Delegate of the United States, noted the good scientific co-operation between the US and Yugoslavia. A special programme has been operating since 1973. In 1986 $1.9 million was provided by the US State Department and, in addition, $0.5 million by the US Department of Agriculture. Yugoslav organisations have been matching these funds. The programme is co-ordinated at the federal level by the responsible body for international co-operation (YUZAMS), but the financing and implementation have taken place at the Republic level. In 1986 this programme had been very satisfactory. In recent years, in order to reduce the risk of fragmentation, projects interesting several Republics and Autonomous Provinces had been launched under the leadership of one scientist. This programme has supported more than 250 projects, with 125 US scientists visiting Yugoslavia for two weeks or more. Some 100 Yugoslavs have gone to US. So far, no other country has benefited from such a programme funded by the US State Department. Mr. Vribalovitch felt that self management was, in itself, not a bad system. It depended very much on the people who ran it at the basic level. Some enterprises were very well run, while others were poorly run, but this depended more on the people than on the system rules.

III. YUGOSLAVIA'S PRINCIPLES PROBLEMS AND OPPORTUNITIES

Professor Galli introduced the discussion on the above topic. It was difficult for the Examiners to grasp the essence of such principles in a one week stay, during the review visit. However, it was essential to tie science, technology and innovation policies to these principles, particularly at a time when the country was reshuffling its economic framework and strategy. Professor Galli re-emphasized some key points made in the Examiners' report:

- The principle of multinationality and the federal structure of Yugoslavia – the diversity of the Federal Units becomes a major problem when it leads to excessively autonomous solutions (e.g. public procurement, technical standards, excellence centres, etc.). On the other hand, a variety of cultures and environments is an asset. Each Federal Unit should try to identify its own role and strengths and problems can be converted into opportunities, as exemplified by the Seismic Institute at Skopje, which has acquired first class competence in earthquake science.

- Self management – major opportunities were offered if appropriate measures were taken (e.g. delegation of responsibility both upward and downward, training, incentives, etc.). The establishment of "quality" or "innovative" circles would constitute one way of developing the creative side of self management. So far the resistance had come not from the workers but, rather, from the medium and high levels of management;

- Non-alignment – the Examiners perceived a feeling of isolation in certain groups and also a danger of seeking excessive technological self-sufficiency. It would be better to develop the capacity to absorb foreign technology and to use Yugoslavia's particular geopolitical situation which, as already mentioned, offered great opportunities for exports to non-aligned countries.

In conclusion, Professor Galli recalled the meaning of the word "crisis" in Chinese, which is made of two overlaping ideograms corresponding to the words "risk" and "opportunity". In a similar vein, in ancient Greek, "crisis" means "alternative" or "choice", and can be depicted as the crest of a mountain separating two slopes.

Mr. Aubert considered that Yugoslavia's founding principles needed to be strengthened and further developed in a positive way. It was important that quick progress be made in view of the role played by Yugoslavia in the international scene. Yugoslavia acted as a critical geopolitical link between East and West, and between North and South, contributing to the cohesion of the world. If these roles were to be maintained, more cohesion was necessary inside Yugoslavia itself. There was room for progress to the extent that Yugoslavia, in its present form, is a young country just a few decades old. But reforms were urgently needed and time was running short.

For *Mrs. Aylward*, self management was in itself a marvellous idea, but in practice the implementation was heavily affected by bureaucracy. It was frequent to see Committees of 100 persons deciding things. She asked how the Yugoslavs could both maintain principles which were so dear to them and at the same time streamline the system.

Mr. Knudsen noted the defensive reactions of the Yugoslav Delegation and expressed some doubt about the capacity of the Yugoslav society to go into action to reform itself, although the problems were clearly identified. Yugoslavia was probably also affected by the "carpet syndrome" observed in many countries (including Denmark). The dust is furtively pushed under the carpet after it has been discovered and no real cleaning is undertaken.

In response to these remarks, *Mr. Matic* denied that the Yugoslav Delegation reactions were defensive. He noted that the press in Yugoslavia had been very critical for some time, opening very large debates in the country, and thus it has not been easy to push "the dust under the carpet". As regards concrete reforms put forward, it was worthwhile mentioning that the losses incurred by enterprises not involved in restructuring were no longer socially covered. Other important measures concerned the establishment of real production costs, and a reduction of government price controls (for the time being 50 per cent of the prices are fixed freely, while 20 per cent are decided by the government and 30 per cent are controlled). Some major issues needed also to be faced: the "non-ownership" approach to social ownership leading to absence of responsibility, the development of bureaucracy and the presence of political factions with too strong an influence on the economy. Principles of self management were genuinely good, but there had been distortions in the socio-political system. The process of adapting the Constitution to make the country more creative was ongoing but was also opposed by established groups including some within the Communist Party. The Party said that there should be no autocratic power, but a number of members behaved like autocrats. The party had to struggle against itself to contribute effectively to the development of Yugoslavia.

Mr. Jones, Chairman of the meeting, expressed warm thanks for these frank and open minded comments, noting that they may reflect both a personal experience with specific groups as well as a long-term view on the evolution of the society as perceived by Minister Matic.

Mr. Vratusa appreciated the efforts made by the Examiners to relate their analysis and recommendations to the basic values and principles of Yugoslavia. However, he was not sure that the wording used in the introductory part of Chapter V reflected fully the essence of these principles. Rather than to say "multinationality, as the basis of the federal structure", it could be more appropriate to say "the federal structure reflecting the multinational character of the country", because multinationality is a fact and not a matter of principle. Rather than say "self management as the organisation model of the society", it could be better to say "socialist self management as the basis of the society", because self management was much broader, in its essence, than an organisation model. And rather than to present "non-alignment as the position towards foreign policy" it could be more appropriate to present "non-alignment as the basis of an independant Yugoslav position on the world affairs". [These changes have now been incorporated in the text].

Comparing the report with other OECD reviews which usually deal deeply with structural and institutional aspects of the scientific systems, *Mr. Matejic* thought that the report lacked some specific assessments and proposals on several critical aspects of the

Yugoslav scientific organisation, e.g. on the Self Management Communities of Interest for Science, on ways to improve their functioning, and on the advisory bodies for science existing in various part of the government machinery. The report did not discuss some key issues such as the ageing of researchers. He felt that some remarks made in the report were inaccurate, e.g. there was a system of metrology and technical standards, but they needed to be modernised. As regards the report's criticism of the absence of federal institutes, the right approach might not be to create federal institutes but to orient activities of existing and future institutes towards national purposes. Mr. Matejic also asked the Examiners to comment on two issues: the administration of the planned Federal Fund for Technological Development and the establishment of a federal advisory council for dealing with licensing matters as proposed in the report.

As regards international dimensions and the role of Yugoslavia as an active "technology bridge", *Mr. Srica* wished to point out the opposition encountered when Yugoslavia asked to enter programmes such as EUREKA, ESPRIT or BRITE. This did not facilitate the integration of Yugoslavia in international technology trends and even pushed it towards technological autarchy. There should be more efforts at international level for open access to world knowledge and know-how, as today's science is tomorrow's technology.

Mr. Marcum emphasized two general features of economic growth today, which may have direct implications for Yugoslav self management. The first feature is that today growth is a "bottom-up" process contrasting with a "top-down" one experienced in the past. Growth occurs from initiative and leadership taken by individuals and small groups. Large organisations and committees cannot generate this genuine dynamism. Paradoxically, self management is well-fitted to encourage "bottom-up" initiatives but it had not done so. Yugoslavs should ask themselves why such a failure has happened and make necessary changes. The second feature is the importance of human capital in the so-called "knowledge-intensive growth" currently being experienced. Thus major efforts are required in training of scientists and engineers and continuous re-education, at all levels including workers at the shopfloor level. The decline of expenditure on higher education in Yugoslavia was a very worrying trend.

Mr. Bell, from the OECD Secretariat, provided comments on several aspects raised by Yugoslav Delegates in relation to OECD work. Firstly, as regards ageing of researchers there was an on-going project – the first results would be available in 1988. One of the biggest problems was unevenness in the hiring of university and institutes research personnel over time. The percentage of the Yugoslav population going to university had been steadily growing over the years. In view of this, there was a need for the research organisations to hire a significant number of new personnel. Secondly, as regards advisory councils for research, the experiences of OECD countries had shown that industry is a good source of advice and could be very influential in improving the work of these councils. Thirdly, as regards international co-operation, this issue would be largely debated at the forthcoming OECD Ministerial Conference in October 1987. Yugoslavia would have an opportunity to again express its concerns.

Mrs. Tvede, Delegate of Denmark, stressed the quality of the Background Report prepared by the Yugoslav Authorities and thought that it should serve as an example to inspire other countries when doing such reviews. She asked what steps would be taken after the review. She noted that, at Yugoslavia's initiative, a workshop under CSTP auspices had been held at OECD in 1986 to study the reviews' methodologies and impacts. It had concluded that their was a need for appropriate follow up to the reviews. The CSTP could have regular workshops of this kind where reviewed countries would report on progress made on responding to OECD recommendations. She also emphasized that the reports prepared for the Yugoslavia's review would be most useful for other OECD countries and that these countries should intensify their efforts to help Yugoslavia in its development.

Professor Galli, responding to the questions from the Yugoslav Delegation, emphasized the need to avoid bureaucracy in the administration of the Federal Fund for Technological Development. The risk of bureaucratisation was very high, as illustrated by the experience of Italy where two large funds were set up. There is now a delay of two to three years between applications and payments to applicants. To avoid this, it would be essential to eliminate any constraints regarding types of research, sectors, etc. to be supported. This would also prevent funding going mainly to large firms, a trend commonly observed with bureaucratic procedures. So the procedure should be as direct, simple, and open as possible. Professor Galli commented also on the ageing problem, in relation to the diffusion of knowledge throughout society. Experience has shown that an excellent vehicle for such a diffusion was individuals who leave companies to create their own firms, in particular to provide advanced services such as marketing, software, engineering, etc. From this point of view, the present situation in Yugoslavia was mediocre and there was a real need to facilitate mobility and entrepreneurship.

In response to general observations made by Mr. Matic, *Mrs. Aylward* recognised that significant changes have occurred since the review visit, and the Examiners' Report reflected to a certain extent the concerns expressed to the Examiners by Yugoslavs during this visit. However, changes were obviously not easy to put forward and required a lot of courage and perseverance. The Federal Strategy for Technological Development should receive the full support of all parties concerned, but needed to be further refined and finalised with more selectivity. As regards the follow-up of the review, she indicated that Ireland had benefited of a similar review in 1985. The concerned minister had decided to set up a small group immediately after the review meeting to make, in a two month period, proposals to implement appropriate recommendations. This approach proved to be very efficient in the Irish context and led to concrete policy measures in a short period.

As regards the administration of the Federal Fund for Technological Development, *Mr. Knudsen* believed that the key thing was to decide beforehand which items would be supported. With Mrs. Aylward, he felt the need for more selectivity, as there were too many projects to be considered. A simple tendering mechanism for supporting a limited number of talented people in well-selected areas could be a good approach. To a certain extent, he disagreed with the view that today's science is tomorrow's technology. Most of technologies for the next 5-10 years were known. The key issue was the application of these technologies. For this, a major problem was the lack of "gap fillers" who need to be flexible and were not generally university people. Denmark has focused on the issue of application of technologies rather than on further advances in research. As regards the global objectives and vision to be pursued, Mr. Knudsen suggested the development of Yugoslavia as a "software" nation. Production of material goods (hard manufacturing) did not have, in the view of Mr. Knudsen, a great future, particularly for smaller countries. Yugoslavia had a niche to exploit in developing the human dimension of economic growth through such aspects as the quality of life, arts, etc., that have tended to be lost in modern economies. "Brain workers" who would develop this "software" nation would not be trained in universities, but through a learning-by-doing process. Moreover, a massive injection in industry of students trained in humanities and social sciences could be very efficient as illustrated by the Danish experience.

In response to questions regarding self-management communities for science and other bodies involved in the management of science in the society, *Mr. Aubert* thought that little could be done to improve the way they functioned, because of more fundamental problems hampering the development of a knowledge-intensive society. These problems, in Mr. Aubert's view, were largely related to the distinction made in the Yugoslav Constitution between the "producers" of knowledge (i.e. the scientists) and the "consumers" of knowledge (i.e. the rest of the population). This distinction was very strange, particularly in a self-management system in which, more than everywhere else, the most crucial knowledge should be generated at "the bottom". Unless this producer/consumer distinction and the related ideology was abandoned, Mr. Aubert felt that there was little chance to develop the creative side of self management. Increasing the knowledge and creativity of all the workers from the bottom up to the top would naturally improve the functioning of the communities for science and similar bodies. A common language would be created between all parties, better informed of needs and capabilities. It would also reduce interference of political factions and bureaucrats in the whole economy.

Mr. Matic thought that the distinction between producers and consumers of knowledge was not so artificial and rigid. Moreover, innovation-oriented activities were strongly encouraged in enterprises by national agreements (social compacts). Continuing education had also been encouraged and special funds had been established in industry for this purpose.

Mr. Varadi agreed that the communities for science were dominated by scientists, and users of research results were in general not well identified. As regards the question of ageing of researchers, Mr. Varadi indicated that the main problem was a reduction in the hiring of young researchers in recent years while criteria for advancement of those already in place were not sufficiently rigorous. He also disagreed on the relationship discussed by the Examiners, between the non-aligned position and the risk of technological self-reliance; there was no policy towards such self-reliance, even if some important technology imports have had negative effects. Finally as regards the metaphor of the carpet, Mr. Varadi thought that the carpet was now well fixed and that it was impossible to push the dust under it, but on the other hand it might be difficult to clean the dust which has already been pushed there.

The chairman of the meeting, *Mr. Jones*, focused the discussion on international co-operation by raising two general issues: what could Yugoslavia do to improve conditions for international co-operation? What could OECD countries do to help Yugoslavia further in concrete terms?

Mr. Strabsic, Director of the Federal Committee for International Co-operation (YUZAMS), express satisfaction at what had been achieved so far. Within the Republics and Provinces, similar committees had been established and the co-ordination was operating well. Re-organisation was under way, leading to the setting-up of an Agency for Technology Transfer. He confirmed that good results had been obtained through the bilateral commission established with US, as well as through the bilateral commission established with EEC. Agreements had been made with other countries and organisations, such as Comecon. New forms of international co-operation had been initiated by Yugoslavia, such as the establishment of the European R&D Co-operation Scheme last year, helping to pull back scientific manpower into industry. The current re-organisation, in the form of the National Agency for Technology Transfer, would consolidate all these efforts. It was hoped that they would not lead to bureaucracy but, on the contrary, towards a strengthening of self-management efforts made at the Republic and Province level, with adequate co-ordination.

Mr. Matic noted that in international co-operation there was a need for participation on an equal footing. Some internal problems and inadequate development in certain fields have prevented Yugoslavia from benefiting from opportunities offered by other countries. However, Mr. Matic pointed out that some OECD countries tend to regard Yugoslavia only as a country to which goods could be sold and not as a place for real co-operation. The position of non-alignment and the openness to the Eastern countries created fears of proliferation of research results, although there were strict mechanisms to prevent this. Yugoslav institutes and enterprises have never been on a "black list". As regards European programmes, BRITE has been closed to Yugoslavia as well as some essential parts of ESPRIT which led to the development of competitive technologies. Mr. Matic hoped that this meeting could be used as a forum to appeal for these programmes to be made more open to Yugoslavia. Current efforts made to restructure the economy and give it a greater market orientation should be recognised by the international community.

Professor Inose recalled some conclusions of a meeting held in Tokyo in November 1983 on international co-operation in science and technology. He stressed that international travel of scientists, and readily available facilities and funds for such travels, should not be considered as a luxury but "a must" for efficient collaboration. Large financial appropriations should be made for exchanges of scientists. However, long-term exchanges of persons have been difficult due to the incompatibility of social systems, including problems of language, housing, etc. OECD countries should make special efforts in this direction. Professor Inose also recalled that a clearing house had been established in the OECD Directorate for Science, Technology and Industry. Although small and new, the clearing house could be a valuable mechanism to be further exploited by Member countries, and particularly Yugoslavia.

Mrs. Kraczwinski agreed that constraining regulations had been explicitly established in some EEC programmes, such as BRITE, preventing Yugoslav participation.

Mr. Alloco, Delegate of the Commission of the European Communities, stressed that it was the intention of EEC to develop comprehensive and fruitful collaboration with Yugoslavia. Good results had been already achieved with YUZAMS as indicated by its Director, as well as with the Committee for Agriculture. The Co-operation Council with EEC to be held in November 1987 would offer the opportunity to raise existing problems.

Mr. Vribalovitch mentioned several examples which showed that the scientific and technological co-operation with Yugoslavia could serve both partners, working on an equal basis. Close co-operation had been established between US agencies and the Maize Institute near Belgrade. This Institute (whose activities were briefly described in the Examiners' Report) had developed particularly resistant crops useful to US farmers who had suffered from frost and other climatic problems. These crops were transfered to US, via Australia, and had helped to restore maize production in US. As another example of the quality of scientific work and competence existing in Yugoslavia, Mr. Vribalovitch mentioned the case of patient with a heart condition who was sent from Zagreb to the Bethesda Hospital near Washington which was supposed to have particular competence in the matter. The patient was finally sent back to the Ljubljana Hospital, whose specialists were considered by US physicians to be the best in the world. This example showed that Yugoslavs needed to recognize competence existing in the different Republics and Provinces, in their own country.

IV. CONCLUSION

Mr. Jones concluded the meeting by a few general observations. On the basis of his own political experience, he noted that modern societies, while recognising the importance of science and technology, were not really receptive to the concrete changes and reforms needed to give them the required status, e.g. in terms of significant budget increases. One possible reason for this could be a lack of scientific and technological culture among politicians and the public at large. Exceptions to this lack of receptiveness seemed to appear only in wartime.

Mr. Jones wondered how much Yugoslav society would need to change in order to cope with the problems which it was now facing. Maybe the crisis needed to be deeper. With regard to inefficient enterprises, Mr. Jones thought that it would be worthwhile to keep in mind the story of a man with a half-dead horse, who finally prefered to kill it completely and buy another one in good health.

Finally, Mr. Jones stressed the importance of cultural change imposed by technological change. New technologies lead to new work practices in enterprises and new divisions of labour in the world economy. These factors impact on Yugoslavia as on other countries. Adaptation is hampered by the fact that one tends to assume that people are not capable of doing things that they have done previously, or not for years. One should not fall in the trap of "one job for life". That applies both to individuals and to countries as a whole.

A Chairman's Summary, presenting the formal conclusions of the meeting appears in Annex I. The list of participants in the meeting can be found in Annex II.

CHAIRMAN'S SUMMARY

Both the General Report prepared by the Yugoslav authorities, and the Examiners' Report drew favourable comment from participants. The meeting felt that recent changes in the economic policies of Yugoslavia and in the science and technology policies and organisation were steps in the right direction.

Fragmentation of the science and technology system

It was agreed that fragmentation of Yugoslavia's science and technology system had to be reduced. More co-operation between research institutions of the different Republics and Provinces is needed. It is essential for smaller OECD countries like Yugoslavia to avoid trying to support too many small projects – all with inadequate funding. The development of national centres of excellence is a priority, for which appropriate funding should be provided. In addition, each Federal Unit needs to recognise the strengths and the competence existing in the other Federal Units.

Importance of non-science and technology factors

The Examiners' Report points out that there is a mistaken tendency to think that the promotion of scientific research is the dominant factor in promoting economic development. While improving Yugoslavia's scientific and technological system is important, many other factors also need urgent attention. The most important of these include motivating management and the workforce, improving the productivity of both, and raising the quality of products and services.

Developing creative self management

The creative side of self management has not been sufficiently developed. So far, self management, as it is applied, deals mainly with income redistribution. Developing further creativity in self management requires the recognition of all workers as sources of knowledge and ideas. This involves, among other things, training efforts and delegation of responsibility to smaller groups, which can take the form of quality circles. Awards and incentives are necessary. If workers have a better understanding of, and greater interest in their day to day jobs, this would help in managing the science and technology system. It may also contribute to reducing political interference in the management of the economy as a whole.

New economic policy directions

The Yugoslav Delegation stressed that the principles of self management were sound, but their implementation was not satisfactory. In particular, the management of the economic system suffers from excessive political interference. Measures already taken, as well as those recently announced to introduce more market forces into the economy, are important steps in the right direction. Production inputs, such as energy, should be priced at market value. The increasing energy use *per capita* in production is against the trend in most advanced economies and needs examination. Special attention should be given to the problem of cost reductions in all areas.

Enterprises that are not able to achieve a competitive position and lack adequate plans for restructuring should be allowed to go bankrupt rather than continue to absorb resources that could be better used elsewhere. Continuing to support such enterprises delays restructuring significantly. The meeting noted that steps had been taken by the Government in this regard.

In addition, the concept of social ownership needs further definition. In particular, social ownership should not be equated with *non*-ownership.

Security, employment and economic dynamism

While recognising the welfare aspects of employment, and the historic commitment of the Federal Socialist Republic to maintaining job security, the meeting questioned the effectiveness of existing work practices. Creating a dynamic economy will be more likely to generate new jobs, even though risk factors must be recognised. An essentially static economy which aims at preserving jobs may actually destroy the ability of the economy to generate wealth.

The question of hiring and firing may be an essential element in making enterprises more dynamic and innovative, taking into account social aspects.

Education

The Chairman of the meeting drew attention to a decline in the number of students graduating in science, as well as to an apparent decrease in quality. He expressed concern as to whether there were sufficient numbers of scientists and engineers being trained to meet Yugoslavia's needs in a technological world which increasingly requires "brain workers". Without recruitment of new professionals, the research community will become increasingly aged and possibly out of touch with new scientific trends.

Priorities and comparative advantages

Smaller countries cannot afford to spread their research and development efforts too thinly on a large spectrum of technologies. They have to be selective and to build on areas where the existence of a skill or resource base gives a natural advantage. Yugoslavia has developed internationally competitive industries in some areas – for example ski equipment, ship hulls, some medical and communication technologies. Some research work in agriculture – for example into disease-resistant sunflowers and high-yield maize – has an international reputation. In the future, Yugoslavia will have to give less attention to goods production and to regonise the importance of "brain-based" services and products with high intellectual content, including design.

Comparative advantage (and disadvantage) should be approached in a broad sense: opportunities often arise unexpectedly. Yugoslavia is in an unique position in world geopolitics in relation to both North-South and to East-West relations. The meeting felt that this should be further developed.

International co-operation

The Yugoslav Delegation agreed with the OECD Examiners on the importance of increasing international co-operation, and expressed its satisfaction as regards current programmes established both with individual Member countries and the EEC, notably in basic research. However, concern was expressed that Yugoslavia was not invited to participate in some new international programmes of a more industrial character. Participation in the EEC programme for research co-operation in manufacturing technologies (BRITE) was singled out as of particular interest to Yugoslavia. The same was said about essential parts of ESPRIT.

Receptiveness to change

The Yugoslav Delegation informed the meeting about the seriousness and the depth of current changes, of actions to be taken as well as expected difficulties and resistance.

One major issue left open by the meeting was the receptiveness of Yugoslav society to the implementation of change. For instance, what will be the extent of the support for increased co-ordination of science and technology policy, and the implementation of this co-ordination? This issue relates to some fundamental aspects of Yugoslav society such as regional autonomy. It might well be that the present crisis needs to become more serious before real reforms can be implemented. This remark applies to other aspects which have already been mentioned, e.g. the bankruptcy problem, or the adaptation of self management.

Less developed parts of Yugoslavia

The Examiners' Report draws attention to the situation of the less developed areas of Yugoslavia, where the problem of receptiveness to change is particularly acute. This subject was not separately discussed but was referred to by several speakers, and by the Yugoslav Delegation which pointed out that technological development represents an essential factor for solving this problem.

LIST OF PARTICIPANTS

Chairman: The Hon. Barry Jones, M.P.,
Minister for Science and Small Business, Australia

YUGOSLAV DELEGATION

Mr. Branko Mikulic,
President of the Federal Executive
Council

Dr. Bozidar Matic,
Member of the Federal Executive
Council,
President of the Federal Committee for
Science and Technology,
Head of Delegation

Dr. Velimir Srica,
President of the Republic Committee
for Science, Technology and
Computer Science SR of Croatia,
Deputy Head of Delegation

Prof. Tibor Varadi,
President,
Association of the Communities of
Science of Yugoslavia

Dr. Antun Vratusa,
Member of the Council of the
Federation,
Member of the Commission for Science
of the Assembly of the SFR of
Yugoslavia

Prof. Bozidar Gluscevic,
Presidency of the Association of
Academies of Science and Arts of
Yugoslavia

Dr. Marijan Strbasic,
Director General,
Federal Administration for
International Scientific, Educational-
Cultural and Technical Co-operation

General Avgust Vrtar,
President of the Council for Science
in the Armed Forces of the SFR of
Yugoslavia

Dr. Mihailo Lasica,
Secretary, Board for Scientific-
Technological Development and
Improvement of Economic Activities,
Economic Chamber of Yugoslavia

Mr. Vlado Drljevic,
Head, Department of Economic
Relations, Federal Secretariat for
Foreign Affairs

Prof. Vlastimir Matejic,
Scientific Councellor at the
"Mihailo Pupin" Institute,
Delegate of the SFR of Yugoslavia
to the CSTP

Mr. Bogic Scepanovic,
Assistant to the President,
Federal Committee for Science and
Technology, Secretary of the Meeting

SCIENTIFIC AND TECHNOLOGICAL POLICY COMMITTEE DELEGATES

Dr. Roy Green,
Australia

His Excellency,
Mr. G. Blancquaert,
Belgium

Ms. Liselotte Tvede,
Denmark

Mr. B. Paulien,
France

Dr. Johanna Krawczynski,
Germany

Prof. Hiroshi Inose,
Japan

Mr. G. Sanz,
Spain

Prof. Hans Landberg
Sweden

Mr. Curt Malmborg,
Sweden

Mr. Andrew Picken,
United Kingdom

Dr. Thomas Vribalobich,
United States

Mr. Vittorino Alloco,
ECC

OECD EXAMINERS

Mrs. Agnes Aylward,
Director,
Science and Technology Policy,
Department of Industry and Trade,
Ireland

Prof. Ricardo Galli,
University of Milan,
Italy

Mr. Morten Knudsen,
Director General,
Technological Institute,
Denmark

Mr. Jean-Eric Aubert, OECD
Science and Technology Policy Division,
Co-ordinator of the review

OECD SECRETARIAT

Mr. John M. Marcum,
Director for Science, Technology and Industry

Mr. John D. Bell,
Head of Science and Technology Policy Division

WHERE TO OBTAIN OECD PUBLICATIONS
OÙ OBTENIR LES PUBLICATIONS DE L'OCDE

ARGENTINA - ARGENTINE
Carlos Hirsch S.R.L.,
Florida 165, 4º Piso,
(Galeria Guemes) 1333 Buenos Aires
Tel. 33.1787.2391 y 30.7122

AUSTRALIA - AUSTRALIE
D.A. Book (Aust.) Pty. Ltd.
11-13 Station Street (P.O. Box 163)
Mitcham, Vic. 3132   Tel. (03) 873 4411

AUSTRIA - AUTRICHE
OECD Publications and Information Centre,
4 Simrockstrasse,
5300 Bonn (Germany)   Tel. (0228) 21.60.45
Gerold & Co., Graben 31, Wien 1 Tel. 52.22.35

BELGIUM - BELGIQUE
Jean de Lannoy,
Avenue du Roi 202
B-1060 Bruxelles   Tel. (02) 538.51.69

CANADA
Renouf Publishing Company Ltd/
Éditions Renouf Ltée,
1294 Algoma Road, Ottawa, Ont. K1B 3W8
Tel: (613) 741-4333
Toll Free/Sans Frais:
Ontario, Quebec, Maritimes:
1-800-267-1805
Western Canada, Newfoundland:
1-800-267-1826
Stores/Magasins:
61 rue Sparks St., Ottawa, Ont. K1P 5A6
Tel: (613) 238-8985
211 rue Yonge St., Toronto, Ont. M5B 1M4
Tel: (416) 363-3171
Federal Publications Inc.,
301-303 King St. W.,
Toronto, Ont. M5V 1J5
Tel. (416)581-1552
Les Éditions la Liberté inc.,
3020 Chemin Sainte-Foy,
Sainte-Foy, P.Q. GIX 3V6,
Tel. (418)658-3763

DENMARK - DANEMARK
Munksgaard Export and Subscription Service
35, Nørre Søgade, DK-1370 København K
Tel. +45.1.12.85.70

FINLAND - FINLANDE
Akateeminen Kirjakauppa,
Keskuskatu 1, 00100 Helsinki 10   Tel. 0.12141

FRANCE
OCDE/OECD
Mail Orders/Commandes par correspondance :
2, rue André-Pascal,
75775 Paris Cedex 16
Tel. (1) 45.24.82.00
Bookshop/Librairie : 33, rue Octave-Feuillet
75016 Paris
Tel. (1) 45.24.81.67 or/ou (1) 45.24.81.81
Librairie de l'Université,
12a, rue Nazareth,
13602 Aix-en-Provence   Tel. 42.26.18.08

GERMANY - ALLEMAGNE
OECD Publications and Information Centre,
4 Simrockstrasse,
5300 Bonn   Tel. (0228) 21.60.45

GREECE - GRÈCE
Librairie Kauffmann,
28, rue du Stade, 105 64 Athens Tel. 322.21.60

HONG KONG
Government Information Services,
Publications (Sales) Office,
Information Services Department
No. 1, Battery Path, Central

ICELAND - ISLANDE
Snæbjörn Jónsson & Co., h.f.,
Hafnarstræti 4 & 9,
P.O.B. 1131 – Reykjavik
Tel. 13133/14281/11936

INDIA - INDE
Oxford Book and Stationery Co.,
Scindia House, New Delhi 110001
Tel. 331.5896/5308
17 Park St., Calcutta 700016   Tel. 240832

INDONESIA - INDONÉSIE
Pdii-Lipi, P.O. Box 3065/JKT.Jakarta
Tel. 583467

IRELAND - IRLANDE
TDC Publishers - Library Suppliers,
12 North Frederick Street, Dublin 1
Tel. 744835-749677

ITALY - ITALIE
Libreria Commissionaria Sansoni,
Via Lamarmora 45, 50121 Firenze
Tel. 579751/584468
Via Bartolini 29, 20155 Milano   Tel. 365083
La diffusione delle pubblicazioni OCSE viene
assicurata dalle principali librerie ed anche da :
Editrice e Libreria Herder,
Piazza Montecitorio 120, 00186 Roma
Tel. 6794628
Libreria Hœpli,
Via Hœpli 5, 20121 Milano   Tel. 865446
Libreria Scientifica
Dott. Lucio de Biasio "Aeiou"
Via Meravigli 16, 20123 Milano Tel. 807679

JAPAN - JAPON
OECD Publications and Information Centre,
Landic Akasaka Bldg., 2-3-4 Akasaka,
Minato-ku, Tokyo 107   Tel. 586.2016

KOREA - CORÉE
Kyobo Book Centre Co. Ltd.
P.O.Box: Kwang Hwa Moon 1658,
Seoul   Tel. (REP) 730.78.91

LEBANON - LIBAN
Documenta Scientifica/Redico,
Edison Building, Bliss St.,
P.O.B. 5641, Beirut   Tel. 354429-344425

**MALAYSIA/SINGAPORE -
MALAISIE/SINGAPOUR**
University of Malaya Co-operative Bookshop
Ltd.,
7 Lrg 51A/227A, Petaling Jaya
Malaysia   Tel. 7565000/7565425
Information Publications Pte Ltd
Pei-Fu Industrial Building,
24 New Industrial Road No. 02-06
Singapore 1953   Tel. 2831786, 2831798

NETHERLANDS - PAYS-BAS
SDU Uitgeverij
Christoffel Plantijnstraat 2
Postbus 20014
2500 EA's-Gravenhage   Tel. 070-789911
Voor bestellingen: Tel. 070-789880

NEW ZEALAND - NOUVELLE-ZÉLANDE
Government Printing Office Bookshops:
Auckland: Retail Bookshop, 25 Rutland Stseet,
Mail Orders, 85 Beach Road
Private Bag C.P.O.
Hamilton: Retail: Ward Street,
Mail Orders, P.O. Box 857
Wellington: Retail, Mulgrave Street, (Head
Office)
Cubacade World Trade Centre,
Mail Orders, Private Bag
Christchurch: Retail, 159 Hereford Street,
Mail Orders, Private Bag
Dunedin: Retail, Princes Street,
Mail Orders, P.O. Box 1104

NORWAY - NORVÈGE
Narvesen Info Center – NIC,
Bertrand Narvesens vei 2,
P.O.B. 6125 Etterstad, 0602 Oslo 6
Tel. (02) 67.83.10, (02) 68.40.20

PAKISTAN
Mirza Book Agency
65 Shahrah Quaid-E-Azam, Lahore 3 Tel. 66839

PHILIPPINES
I.J. Sagun Enterprises, Inc.
P.O. Box 4322 CPO Manila
Tel. 695-1946, 922-9495

PORTUGAL
Livraria Portugal,
Rua do Carmo 70-74,
1117 Lisboa Codex   Tel. 360582/3

**SINGAPORE/MALAYSIA -
SINGAPOUR/MALAISIE**
See "Malaysia/Singapor". Voir
« Malaisie/Singapour »

SPAIN - ESPAGNE
Mundi-Prensa Libros, S.A.,
Castelló 37, Apartado 1223, Madrid-28001
Tel. 431.33.99
Libreria Bosch, Ronda Universidad 11,
Barcelona 7   Tel. 317.53.08/317.53.58

SWEDEN - SUÈDE
AB CE Fritzes Kungl. Hovbokhandel,
Box 16356, S 103 27 STH,
Regeringsgatan 12,
DS Stockholm   Tel. (08) 23.89.00
Subscription Agency/Abonnements:
Wennergren-Williams AB,
Box 30004, S104 25 Stockholm Tel. (08)54.12.00

SWITZERLAND - SUISSE
OECD Publications and Information Centre,
4 Simrockstrasse,
5300 Bonn (Germany)   Tel. (0228) 21.60.45
Librairie Payot,
6 rue Grenus, 1211 Genève 11
Tel. (022) 31.89.50
United Nations Bookshop/Librairie des Nations-
Unies
Palais des Nations,
1211 – Geneva 10
Tel. 022-34-60-11 (ext. 48 72)

TAIWAN - FORMOSE
Good Faith Worldwide Int'l Co., Ltd.
9th floor, No. 118, Sec.2
Chung Hsiao E. Road
Taipei   Tel. 391.7396/391.7397

THAILAND - THAILANDE
Suksit Siam Co., Ltd., 1715 Rama IV Rd.,
Samyam Bangkok 5   Tel. 2511630
INDEX Book Promotion & Service Ltd.
59/6 Soi Lang Suan, Ploenchit Road
Patjumamwan, Bangkok 10500
Tel. 250-1919, 252-1066

TURKEY - TURQUIE
Kültur Yayinlari Is-Türk Ltd. Sti.
Atatürk Bulvari No: 191/Kat. 21
Kavaklidere/Ankara   Tel. 25.07.60
Dolmabahce Cad. No: 29
Besiktas/Istanbul   Tel. 160.71.88

UNITED KINGDOM - ROYAUME-UNI
H.M. Stationery Office,
Postal orders only: (01)211-5656
P.O.B. 276, London SW8 5DT
Telephone orders: (01) 622.3316, or
Personal callers:
49 High Holborn, London WC1V 6HB
Branches at: Belfast, Birmingham,
Bristol, Edinburgh, Manchester

UNITED STATES - ÉTATS-UNIS
OECD Publications and Information Centre,
2001 L Street, N.W., Suite 700,
Washington, D.C. 20036 - 4095
Tel. (202) 785.6323

VENEZUELA
Libreria del Este,
Avda F. Miranda 52, Aptdo. 60337,
Edificio Galipan, Caracas 106
Tel. 951.17.05/951.23.07/951.12.97

YUGOSLAVIA - YOUGOSLAVIE
Jugoslovenska Knjiga, Knez Mihajlova 2,
P.O.B. 36, Beograd   Tel. 621.992

Orders and inquiries from countries where
Distributors have not yet been appointed should be
sent to:
OECD, Publications Service, 2, rue André-Pascal,
75775 PARIS CEDEX 16.

Les commandes provenant de pays où l'OCDE n'a
pas encore désigné de distributeur doivent être
adressées à :
OCDE, Service des Publications. 2, rue André-
Pascal, 75775 PARIS CEDEX 16.

71784-07-1988

OECD PUBLICATIONS, 2, rue André-Pascal, 75775 PARIS CEDEX 16 - No. 44295 1988
PRINTED IN FRANCE
(92 88 04 1) ISBN 92-64-13138-8